May Your First Love
Be Your Last

Gregory Clark

May Your First Love Be Your Last

and Other Stories

McClelland and Stewart Limited   Toronto/Montreal

Third Printing 1973

The stories in this volume were
first published in *Weekend Magazine*.

Photographs in the preliminary section are
by Louis Jaques, *Weekend Magazine*.

Illustrations on pages 48-49, 110, 118, 122-23,
143, 159, 167, 213 reproduced by courtesy
of Jack Tremblay, and illustrations on pages
57, 65 and 92 reproduced by courtesy of
Edwin McNally.

0-7710-2109-7

The Canadian Publishers
McClelland and Stewart Limited
25 Hollinger Road, Toronto 374

Printed and bound in Canada
by *John Deyell Limited*

Contents

Introduction

It is nice to be able to report
that Gregory Clark is alive
and well and living in a hotel
suite in Toronto.

Sarah Louise Greig, age 18, on the occasion of her engagement to Joseph Thomas Clark.

The reason I mention this is that as Gregory Clark has been around almost since type was invented, or so it seems, to this day I still have people asking me if he is alive. In fact, so many people had asked me this recently – "surely those Clark stories you run in *Weekend* are repeats," they say, just as though Greg was some kind of a TV show – that I hied myself to Toronto to find out. There I knocked on a certain door (you must knock quite sharply, because Greg doesn't always hear you the first time these days) in the King Edward Hotel, and was ushered in, to spend a couple of days in the Wonderful World of Gregory Clark.

At first glance it is quite easy to understand why many people do not think Gregory Clark does exist, or ever did exist. After all, he is a most improbable sight. There he is, all five feet two of him. His fine, white hair looks a bit like a halo – although Greg is not exactly the halo-type – as he stands with his back to the light coming through his sitting room window.

That sophisticated man-about-town, Joseph Thomas Clark, Christmas, 1892 (possibly Easter, 1893).

Then you notice his eyes. They are small grey eyes, peering up through the tangled white brows. And even though Greg is now seventy-six these eyes are bright, inquisitive, seldom still. They are very young eyes with that quality you see in the eyes of mischievous boys – they are watching you closely to catch you doing something that will make their owner laugh. They are daring you to say something pompous.

Once in the room, Greg says, "You'll need a little drink before lunch," settling into his easy chair, strategically placed so that his whiskey and tobacco and pipes are on his right, his books within easy reach behind him, and the TV set at eyeball level across the room.

Greg hands me the bottle. "I think it is an insult to pour a man his own drink."

I look at the label and whistle softly in appreciation. "Glad to see you're not suffering."

"I pay a little more and drink a little less."

Greg, age 5, and
Little Joe, 2.

"Maybe," I venture, "you shouldn't be drinking at all? If you aren't supposed to drink, don't worry about me. I've had lunch on an empty stomach before."

"I haven't heard that expression since my Grandmother Greig died," Greg says. "That's what she always said, 'never eat on an empty stomach' – and I've tried to obey her all my life."

Greg smiles piously, happy to be able to prove that he has always obeyed his elders. But that lasts no more than a moment and then he adds:

"Don't worry about me. After my last heart attack – it should have carried me off but it didn't for some reason – I was getting ready to leave the hospital. My doctor, Bill Oille, was sitting on the foot of my bed looking at me with those marble eyes of his.

" 'Greg,' he said, 'we've got to keep those heart muscles and valves relaxed. Now, in most cases I recommend pills. But you can have a choice, pills or whiskey.'

The family:
Greg, age 8,
Joe, 5, and
Mabel, 2.

"I never bothered replying. So now I have two drinks before lunch and two drinks before dinner – to relax my heart."

There is a pause as Greg pours himself his first drink. Then those small, bright eyes peer over the steel rims of his old-fashioned specs and he adds:

"Of course, I never told Bill I always drink doubles."

I explain to Greg that many of his fans and friends were worried that he would find life in a hotel a lonely existence. Greg sold his big, old house and moved into the hotel a few years ago after the death of his wife.

But I am happy to say that Greg, in a hotel, is approximately as lonely as the Beatles when they are on tour.

"When you first move into a hotel as a permanent resident," he explains, "you spend the first month looking at the other permanent residents as you meet them. The second month you smile and say hello. The third month you start joining them for meals.

13

The first love
and the last love.

"There is my friend, Leonard Leslie, for instance. A fine man. I looked at him for the regulation one month, smiled and said hello for the regulation second month and then, at the start of the third month, I sat beside him as he ordered breakfast.

" 'How did you lose your left arm?' I asked, just like that. 'Passchendaele,' he said. So we had no trouble. I was at Passchendaele myself."

Then there is the hotel staff.

It starts with the chambermaid on his floor. As we walk down the hall the first day, he waves to her and says, loud enough for her to hear, "She checks my room about four times a day – she expects to come in some day and find me dead."

The chambermaid indignantly denies this.

At the desk in the hotel lobby, Greg stops to pick up two packages of the tobacco he has sent to him specially

Lieutenant 4th C.M.R.,
France, 1917.

from a tobacconist in London. The security man comes along and says, "Mr. Clark, don't tell me you're still smoking that stuff?"

Greg's head tilts back so he can look up into this tormentor's face, his eyebrows bristle and twitch with a fine case of fake indignation. It's a scene, I feel, that has been played quite a few times before.

Greg defends his choice of tobacco. The security man turns to me for help, saying:

"One night one of my men came to me and said there was a fire in Mr. Clark's room. It smelled like a mattress burning. So I raced along and opened the door without taking the time to knock – and there was Mr. Clark, sitting and watching TV and puffing on his pipe.

"And my man was right. It did smell as though a mattress was burning in his room."

It really doesn't matter in which dining room one eats with Greg. In one, for instance, there is the darkly hand-

The late Victor Sifton,
Adjutant of
the 4th C.M.R., 1917,
and Greg,
his assistant.

some waitress who keeps Greg posted on the latest Gypsy jokes.

(Gypsy jokes? I know there are Polish jokes and Elephant jokes. But Gypsy jokes?)

In another there is an equally handsome waitress who bullies him a bit. One day he wants a light lunch made up mainly of a sandwich which is two slices of toasted bread holding two pancakes which, in turn, hold scrambled eggs. The whole thing is covered with melted butter and maple syrup and is delicious.

But the waitress reminds Greg that he had eggs for breakfast and should have something else for lunch.

"Too many eggs make you bilious," she warns.

In the main dining room Greg's entrance touches off a minor eruption. The entire staff converges on him.

"See," he says, "They think the old man is going to splurge."

Daughter Elizabeth, age 3, with her dog, Sally. "It is a 'Damnation' dog," she would explain gravely.

Then he turns, points to me, and says:

"But I'm not paying, boys. He's paying. So the sky's the limit."

We don't go out on the street during this visit, because it is hot and very close and Greg will admit, reluctantly, that he occasionally suffers from fatigue these days. But I know what happens when he does go out because his long-time feuding and fishing friend Gillis Purcell, General Manager of The Canadian Press, tells me:

"When Greg goes out he is constantly stopped by people who come up and shake his hand and say hello. So this day he is going along, being stopped about every ten steps, when a man steps up and presses a couple of dollars into Greg's hand.

"For once Greg is speechless. But he recovers and explains to the man that he doesn't need the money. The man says, 'No need to say anything – I watched you coming

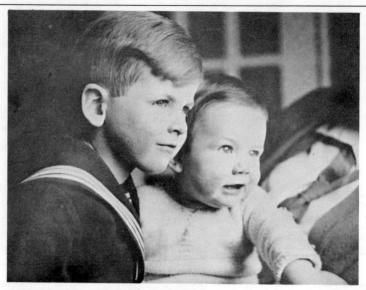

Sons Murray and Greg Junior.

along just now, stopping all those people. You're probably one of those local characters who work the downtown area."

"Well, that did shut Greg up. He never said a word until he got back to his room. Then he exploded. 'Goddammit,' he said, 'that man insulted me. He called me a local character. And everyone knows I'm a national character.' "

So most of the time during this visit we sit in his room and talk. That's what Greg does best – talk. I feel he talks even better than he writes. It is pleasant to sit there in his tidy suite (sitting room, bedroom and bath) and gently encourage him to tell how Gregory Clark became a national character and, to my knowledge, Canada's only living leprechaun.

"It all began in 1930," Greg recalls. "That was a terrible time in Toronto. The Depression had arrived, and all those people who had come to the big city from their villages and farms were scared and homesick.

Greg Senior and Greg Junior.

"The paper reflected this. There was nothing in it every day but bad news, scary news. One day Mr. Bone, the managing editor of the Toronto *Daily Star*, was leafing through the latest issue of the *Star Weekly*. He turned to Mr. Cranston, the managing editor of the *Weekly*, and said: 'Mr. Cranston, my first responsibility is the *Daily*. But I am also supposed to keep an eye on the *Weekly*. And I'm telling you, Mr. Cranston, there is only one single cheerful thing in this issue.'

"With that, Mr. Bone pointed a finger at Jimmie Frise's cartoon, Birdseye Centre. There was no Depression in Birdeye Centre. The people there had never heard of the Depression. It was the village, I guess, where all those frightened people in Toronto wished they could return to.

" 'I want to see more of this,' Mr. Bone said, his finger still pointing at Birdseye Centre. Then he walked back into his office.

"Mr. Cranston was in a sweat. Surely Mr. Bone didn't

With Helen at Pelee Island, amid a blizzard of pheasants.

With large-mouth bass at Go Home Bay.

mean that we were to carry two Birdseye Centres? So he called us all together. He told the writers that somebody had to write some copy to justify another, and different, Jimmie Frise cartoon.

"Well, most of the writers thought that was undignified, to write copy merely to support a cartoon. Nobody volunteered. So I said I would try it. That's how I got my real start – as a prop for a Jimmie Frise cartoon."

As you sit and listen, you know this isn't exactly the whole truth and nothing but the truth. You know that while Jimmie Frise was a warm and wonderful cartoonist, Greg's words were more than "props." You also know that if Jimmie Frise was alive today he would tell you this. But it is Greg's story, and who am I to challenge him?

All I remember about those far-off days is bugging my mother every Saturday in our small Nova Scotia town to be sure and buy the Toronto *Star Weekly* so I could read the latest adventures of Jim and Greg. Which, I guess,

while it did not make me an authority, did make me a member of what was then Canada's fastest-growing, non-exclusive club – the fans of Jim and Greg.

Mr. Bone and Mr. Cranston had been right. The people of Toronto, and the people everywhere, wanted to forget the Depression and their troubles, at least momentarily. The circulation of the *Star Weekly* climbed steadily and Jim and Greg were there, each Saturday, on the back page of the paper getting into hilarious jams.

It was then that the Gregory Clark we know today began to evolve.

"Jim needed me as a cartoon character," Greg explains, going on with his story after carefully re-filling his pipe with his special, sent-from-London brand of mattress stuffing. Which is a succinct way of telling how one of this country's most distinctive sartorial creations came to life.

I mean, this is why a pork-pie hat perches atop fuzzy white sideburns, why the now-thickening five-foot-two

Trout-fishing with Chief Justice Sir William Mulock at *his* pond.

frame is still swathed in a veritable rainbow of colours, why the right hand invariably grips a gnarled cane and why, even at seventy-six, the walk is one of cocky jauntiness.

That is the Gregory Clark Jimmie Frise envisaged, and that is the Gregory Clark that came about.

Mind you, this has caused confusion amongst his friends. Some insist that there is no such person as Greg Clark – that Greg Clark is a man-made creation.

But this really isn't so. Greg is simply a much more complex person than he appears on the surface, and back in 1920, long before the Frise version of Clark began to appear, such an experienced observer of the human scene as Ernest Hemingway was baffled by Clark. Clark had been friendly and encouraging to the youthful Hemingway when he first began to write for the Toronto *Star*, and one day Hemingway wrote this about the baffling little man he had come in contact with:

Trout-fishing with Mary Pickford.

He loves his wife and his baby. He loves hunting and fishing and fishing tackle. He loves guns and books about guns . . . He also loves to think. He thinks very well but he never strains himself. He likes it about Canada, too. What I dislike he dislikes too but it does not touch him . . . Greg is very romantic. But I can never understand all the way inside of him because he is romantic. I am romantic too and that is the trouble. You cannot dismiss him or classify him because he is always acting and you cannot tell how much of it is acting. He also acts inside himself. He is an officer and a gentleman. It is better that way. He does things for people . . . There is too much India rubber in him. I have never seen him angry . . . If he has a weakness it is having too much sense. He writes the best of anyone on the paper. I have known him a long time but I do not know much about him.

Greg, had he known at that time what Hemingway had written, would have been particularly touched by the line: "He writes the best of anyone on the paper." Because Greg never really felt he belonged in newspaper work. He still insists he got into the business "through the back door" – his father was editor-in-chief when he joined in 1911.

Even World War I, in which he distinguished himself by winning the Military Cross and rising to the rank of major, did not give him the confidence he felt he needed to become a first-class newspaper writer. But it did give him his start as a story-teller.

Some of his better anecdotes stem from that time. And, just as there was no Depression in his writings of the Dirty Thirties, so there is little of the horror that was World War I in his stories about his years under fire. He tells you, for instance, that he got his commission because the sergeant-major in charge of the awkward squad, noticing Greg's difficulties in handling the heavy Ross rifle, re-

Trout-fishing
in the Humber River
with the
late Robert Heart.

ported to the commanding officer: "Sir, that little soʙ will never make a soldier. You will have to make him an officer."

He obviously never regretted his choice. Years later he was to recall:

"Greg's leadership was exercised by intelligence and his discipline was enforced by affection. The men in his platoon called him Tom Thumb and it was not an unusual sight to see him perched on the shoulders of his platoon sergeant, who was a giant, being transported through the mud that was too deep for him to navigate himself. This strange feat could be accomplished by Greg with no loss of authority."

But Greg refuses, in this as in most other instances, to take his role too seriously. He tells you, for example, that he won the м.c. because "I could run faster, jump higher, and lie flatter than any other man in the regiment."

Army records, however, show that he won the coveted

Gordon Sinclair, Frederick Griffin and Greg.

M.C. at Vimy. It was an immediate award and the citation, praising his conspicuous gallantry and devotion to duty, sums it up like this:

"He assumed command of and led his Company with great ability, gained his objective and consolidated the position. He set a fine example of courage and initiative."

Greg, of course, doesn't talk that way – it smacks too much of officialdom. But fifty years later, to commemorate that frightful but magnificent accomplishment Canadians now dimly recall as Vimy, Greg wrote a vignette for *Week-end Magazine* to tell new generations of readers what that particular incident meant to him – as a Canadian. He wrote:

Fifty years is a long time to keep memory green. Yet, to me there is still a mystique about Vimy Ridge. I think it is because Vimy was and is a symbol.

First, it was a symbol to the Germans. When in September and October, 1914, their mighty sweep

Cowboy Keane daring Greg to eat canned rattlesnake.

across Flanders and France was stemmed, one of the things they held on to with desperate determination was the nine-mile-long Vimy Ridge, running north and south and making a sort of bastion of their line of conquest across France. Then they fortified it with all the military engineering skill they could command. It became a fortress. It became a symbol. Time and again, in 1915, the French assaulted it, in vain. In 1916, the British attacked it. The gentle slope – on our side – of Vimy Ridge became a vast cemetery of French, British and Germans. The Germans held it. And the German nation at home knew all was well. They had Vimy Ridge.

It became a symbol to Canadians when, in the autumn of 1916, the four divisions of our corps straggled north from the Somme, exhausted and sadly reduced. We were spaced up along the front of Vimy Ridge of all places. What a place to re-fresh a battle-

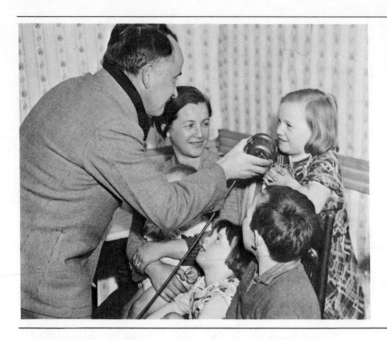

weary corps! We could not dig a bit of new trench
without disinterring the bodies of French, British or
Germans. And the decaying French trenches were dis-
solving into the mud. The whole 7,000 yards of front
we were spread along crawled with bloated, scabby rats.
The Germans facing us up that gentle slope were
secure in their vast trench system reinforced with concrete. Beyond the crest of the rise lay the true Ridge, a
sudden steep cliff-like slope behind which the Germans
had their howitzers. Beyond that lay plains of villages,
invisible to us, comfortable.

A long, dirty winter lay ahead. Vimy became a symbol of war's filth and futility. Before winter was half
over, we knew what our next battle was to be.

It was to become a new symbol. THE symbol! We
were to take this massive, impregnable bastion of
German might and power.

Easter Sunday night – how is THAT for symbolism? – we were moved from our resting places back of the line and our jumping-off positions.

The whole Corps! For the first time in our history, the four Canadian divisions lined up along that infernal and stinking front, shoulder to shoulder, from away down near Arras across 7,000 yards of the great German bastion's foot, in order from south to north. First, Second, Third, and Fourth Divisions.

There is symbolism for you. Canadians from the Atlantic to the Pacific, a solid line.

At 5:30 A.M., April 9, in a sleet and snow blizzard, the volcano of our artillery erupted.

Behind the wall of fire we floundered up the ruined, filthy slope.

We took the Ridge. In the next three days we went 4,500 yards, took 4,000 prisoners, 54 cannon, 104 trench mortars, 124 machine guns.

We lost 3,598 killed and more than 7,000 wounded.

Symbols are costly.

My battalion of the Third Division reached the crest at 7:05 A.M. I was the only surviving officer, and my company and I had the proud distinction of leading its first platoon across the crest to establish a Lewis-gun strong point down that steep, brushy, wooded hill.

The sleet and snow miraculously ceased, the sun came out. It was a stupendous sight. There below us, like the kingdoms of the earth, lay the Douai plain for miles.

And I thought it was symbolic – ah, that's the word! – symbolic, that we had done it at Easter.

As far as I could see, south, north, along the miles of Ridge, there were the Canadians. And I experienced my first full sense of nationhood.

That was a small, but moving bit written to mark

Toronto Star war veterans
in Paris during
Vimy pilgrimage, 1937.

War correspondent Greg,
leaving Russell Square Hotel,
London, on May 6th, 1940.
He was to reach G.H.Q. at Arras,
France, the day the roof
fell in on Rotterdam.

what Greg thought was an important anniversary – not
for him – but for all Canadians. As you can see, with the
one exception of mentioning that he had "the proud distinction" of leading his men over the fearsome crest, he
never once talked about what had happened to him on that
terrible morning.

In fact, only occasionally, as he reminisces, will the
listener hear an echo of what it was like to be small and
frightened and yet burdened with the obligation to command, in that holocaust. It was late afternoon – dusk is the
time for certain types of memories to take shape – when he
told me this bitter/humorous anecdote:

"We were in a shell hole, I was the officer in charge.
Two of my men were dead beside me, a couple were
wounded. I was hunting through my gear for my iron
rations – a can of cold beans made in Canada. Naturally, I
had forgotten to bring the can with me. One of my men

nodded to a dead soldier and said, 'Use his – he isn't going to need anything.' So I did. And as I bit down on a mouthful of cold beans my molar hit a pebble, and broke. The agony was terrible.

"I learned later that the loyal Canadian who made these beans for the troops was in the habit of having his staff mix small pebbles in with the beans. It brought the cans up to the legal weight and made him a little extra profit.

"To this day, every time I see a portrait of this famous Canadian, I draw myself up at attention, face the portrait and let loose with a loud raspberry.

"People think I'm crazy when they see me do this, but I can't help it."

Greg is mainly content, however, to leave philosophy to the pundits. Bruce West, Toronto *Globe and Mail* columnist, recalls that Greg was appalled, when entering the newspaper profession, by the number of heavy thinkers writing on the problems of the world.

With the late Lieutenant Murray Clark, Q.O.R., attached to Regina Rifles.

"I decided," Greg told Bruce, "that someone should sit in a corner of the newspaper and play marbles, just to help the reader keep his balance."

Again, this is true – but not completely true. All the while Greg was "playing marbles" in his corner of the *Star Weekly* with Jimmie Frise, he was also building a solid reputation as senior reporter and feature writer with the *Daily Star*.

While he never missed a week with his regular column, he also tramped the world to talk with kings and commoners, to field marshals and privates, to pillars of the professional world and to the derelicts along Skid Row.

He once told Douglas Amaron, now a senior news executive with The Canadian Press: "In the great campaigns of war and peace it is the privates, corporals and sergeants who eventually have to carry out the hard work – not the generals. If you cultivate their respect and friendship, they won't let you down."

Greg with Matt Halton
and daughter Kathleen,
now wife of critic
and dramatist Kenneth Tynan.

During these years Greg not only met an astonishing number of people, he made and kept an astonishing number of friends. All kinds of friends. A hunting pal of Greg's, Alex Forbes, of Hespeler, Ontario, testifies to this. He remembers when the two were shopping in New York one day, he saw Greg across the store shaking hands, chuckling and chatting with another man. Suddenly Greg shouted:

"Hey, Alex, come over here. I want you to meet a friend of mine."

Forbes did as he was asked and met for the first time Edward, Duke of Windsor, a man Greg has interviewed three times.

As you can see by now, a mere two-day stay with a man like Gregory Clark is not nearly enough. For instance, we hadn't even mentioned fishing. And not to mention fishing in his presence is somewhat like forgetting to mention hockey when talking with Jean Beliveau.

Greg with his late brother, Joe, director of Public Relations for Canadian Armed Services at Vasco, Italy.

But I had a problem. I am not a fisherman. Gregory Clark is *the* fisherman. Once he and *Weekend Magazine* Photo Editor Louis Jaques fished one of Scotland's most famous salmon streams all during the daylight hours of a dreary, rainy day. No salmon.

That night they stopped at an inn where Greg insisted that if they couldn't catch a Scottish salmon they would at least eat a Scottish salmon. The salmon was served.

It was canned salmon – canned in Russia.

Just like everything else he does, Greg uses his fishing experiences to show himself as always the gentle loser. The little guy the fates have combined against – in a benign sort of way, of course. So it is difficult to visualize what it would be like to go fishing with him – especially as all his closest fishing friends are also story tellers.

Once, I remember, I bumped into the late Ralph Allen – one of Canada's finest writers – at a cocktail party. I knew Ralph had just returned from a fishing trip with

Greg, world traveller, pauses for a contemplative moment outside the gates of London's Clarence House.

Left to right: Gillis Purcell, Bruce West, and Alec Forbes.

Greg. So I asked how things had gone.

Ralph looked at me coldly. "I don't want to hear Greg Clark's name mentioned," he said. "He is the sneakiest, the slipperiest, the most conniving, the most under-handed, the most abominable, the . . ."

But here he stopped to have a swallow so I was able to retreat. Later, I told Greg about this and he listened closely and chuckled. He wasn't upset a bit.

"I knew I had got to him," he said. "You see, he thought he had caught the biggest fish and he had left this fish in a pond he had built at the edge of the lake, and that night – why, that night some unknown renegade went in the dark and let that fish loose."

Greg sat and thought about that foul deed for a moment, and the terrible renegade who could do that to a fishing friend. Then he added:

"So the next day when we judged the fish Ralph was terribly upset when my fish was the biggest."

That was the way it went on the Greg Clark fishing trips. People such as Greg and Gil Purcell and Bruce West and Ralph Allen and Chief Carpenter and Joffre Dechene went out into the wilds not only to outwit the trout. They went there to outwit each other. They did this for years and enjoyed each fiendish moment. And referred to my friend Greg as "Sneaky Clark."

But time is running short and I have to remind him that so far we aren't even up to World War II. Greg, never one to give an inch, says, "That's your fault, you tell too many stories."

But then he settles deeper into his chair and remembers that despite being forty-seven and having a family — he then had a wife, two sons, Murray and Gregory, and one daughter, Elizabeth — he was en route overseas three months after war was declared in 1939.

He says there wasn't too much to this war, personally, that is. There was Dunkerque and the deadly fighting

Fly-fishing with the late Jimmy Frise in the Laurentide Park, Quebec.

Greg repairing the gum on his Indian birch-bark canoe.

amongst the peaks and valleys of Italy, and D-Day. "But this time I was only writing."

But this time there was personal tragedy. A few days before his birthday, when Greg had planned to show him the Paris he had known and loved, his son Murray, an infantry lieutenant, was killed in action on the western front.

Greg left the war. He knew his place was with his wife back in Toronto.

It could be, too, that this sad shock – and the resulting lull in what had been a continuously hectic life – led Greg to do some serious thinking about what he was going to do with the rest of his life.

Whatever the reason, he and Jimmie Frise – at an age when many men are thinking of pension benefits – decided to make a move.

"I wasn't at all happy," Greg recalls, "so I phoned John McConnell (publisher of *The Standard* in Montreal,

which developed into today's *Weekend Magazine*) and asked if we could come aboard. John said, 'Come and see me.'

"We had a wonderful meeting in Montreal with Glenn Gilbert (then editorial director of *The Standard*), and that was probably the only newspaper contract signed while the participants were lying on the floor.

"Glenn took me to the station in a wheelchair while I bowed and waved my porkpie hat to the crowds. It was quite a day."

Greg pauses for a moment, then says:

"I hate to spoil a good story, but everybody says it was my idea that Jim and I should resign on Christmas Eve — you know, to make up for that famous wholesale Christmas Eve firing at the *Star*. (It is a newspaper legend that on a Christmas Eve late in the Dirty Thirties, Hindmarsh fired over twelve of his new staff.) But it wasn't my idea. It was Jim's.

"We were sitting on the train, coming home, a little subdued now we realized we were going to leave the *Star* after all those years. Jim said, 'Greg, you'll tell Hindmarsh?'

" 'No,' I said, 'you tell him.'

"Jim thought about this for a moment and then said: 'All right. I will. I'll tell him Christmas Eve.' "

A year later, Jimmie Frise died.

"I was completely lost," Greg tells me. "I couldn't see how I could carry on without that old, familiar format — the Frise cartoon with my story going with it.

"But Craig (Craig Ballantyne, former Editorial Director of *Weekend*) came up with the suggestion I write a weekly feature, about 600 words, at the back of the book. I didn't think it would work, not without Jimmy. I really didn't."

But it did work and this regular full-page "shortie," plus his daily column "Packsack," which appeared in

Greg is presented with
a salmon at the
Ottawa Press Club.

scores of Canadian daily newspapers, made him the most widely-read Canadian ever.

Today, of course, Greg has cut down on his writing chores. The "Packsack" no longer appears. His *Weekend* articles appear about once a month.

But while his physical limitations have brought this about, his mental muscles are still in fine shape. His stuff is getting better, and one editor has told Greg, "By 1980 you should be just about hitting your peak."

There was, in fact, a recent incident to prove this. When John Lennon and his entourage came to Canada to stage a sleep-in for peace in Montreal, the first stop was Greg's King Edward Hotel in Toronto.

That evening Greg was asleep – in the raw, as he terms it. There was a knock on his door. Because of his nude condition, Greg opened the door only a mere crack. At the door were three young men, all with beards.

"We," said the leader, politely, "wish to interview Mr. Lennon."

"Lenin!" Greg exclaimed. "Why, Lenin has been dead for forty-five years. I once met Trotsky, but I never laid *eyes* on Lenin . . ."

"No, no," cut in the young man. "I mean Lennon, of the Beatles."

"The beetles," said Greg. "Ah, they are the Coleoptera. I am a Lepidopterist. I believe you have called at the wrong room."

And the three young men left hastily, wondering what kind of over-age anarchist they had aroused.

This example of Greg's mental agility is one good reason why I never personally take part in a controversy that constantly rages around the bantam-like figure of Canada's favourite story teller. Sad, but true, he has often been accused of letting imagination run wild with fact —

A banquet in Montreal to celebrate Greg's fiftieth year in journalism. Left: Editorial Director Craig Ballantyne; right: John G. McConnell, publisher of *Weekend Magazine*.

Greg

"all those things couldn't happen to one person," is the usual plaint.

Once, when I was younger and brasher, I did bring up this point. I listened to Greg tell a story and finally said:

"Greg, the last time you told that story you had it at Passchendaele. Now it is the Somme."

Greg, the picture of outrage, turned on me and said:

"I'm merely rearranging my geography a bit – the way God would if he was a story teller."

So on this visit I left this subject alone. But I did get my come-uppance, anyway. Greg told me about how he inadvertently helped a man make a killing in the stock market. It was a very funny, but seemingly implausible tale.

But I had learned my lesson. I did not say a word. And then, at breakfast one morning, Greg and I sat with his friend Leslie. Leslie asked me:

Governor-General Michener at the presentation of the Service Medal of the Order of Canada.

"Has Greg told you about how he helped a fellow make all that money, and he himself didn't make a cent?"

I said he had. I also couldn't resist suggesting that maybe, just maybe, our old friend Greg was, well, playing God again.

Leslie denied that vehemently. "After all," he said, "I was with him when it happened."

I will say this for Greg. He did not rub it in, or say "I told you so."

He simply sat there looking infuriatingly pious and righteous. So pious and righteous, I am delighted to add, his waitress rushed up and said:

"Mr. Clark, I told you not to have two eggs. You know they always make you bilious."

That took him down a peg.

Frank Lowe
Editor, *Weekend Magazine*
Montreal, September 1969

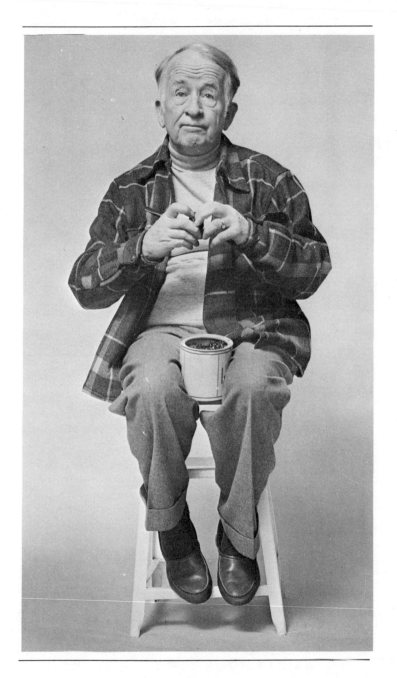

May Your First Love Be Your Last

By and large, I have had little trouble with the fair sex.

I mean, of course, that they have troubled little with me.

Being the first-born of my family, I was naturally a Mamma's Boy. By the time I was five, I already realized, dimly, my responsibility to demonstrate to the younger members of the family, arriving, how to behave. By the time I was eight, I did not have to be told about Tuesdays and Fridays. On Tuesdays and Fridays I put out the ash cans and garbage cans as a matter of course. I wrestled them out to the curb, though I was a shrimp, or whiffet (as we small ones were called). By the age of ten my senses were so acute that at six o'clock in the morning, I could hear the soft snowflakes beating upon the attic bedroom window. Softly I would rise. Softly I would dress, waking neither my young brother and sister, nor my parents. And the first shovel you heard on Howland avenue, at 7 A.M., was mine. All the mothers of Howland avenue admired me.

They pointed me out as a model to their sons. And I was beaten up as a matter of course and frequently had a bloody nose. I was an object of contempt to my generation.

By the time I was twelve, I was so covered with freckles — face, shoulders, arms, hands — that you could hardly see me. From amidst the freckles, my piggy blue eyes looked out eagerly. But nobody looked back. Especially the fair

sex. I was spared those grim years of adolescence. No girls troubled me.

Now, do not think I was lonely. Forlorn? Well, maybe a little; but we all must feel forlorn one time or another in our lives. Fortunately, on the next street, Albany avenue, lived two older boys named Hoyes Lloyd and Stuart Thompson who became in their time two of the greatest field naturalists of Canada. They were glad of a queue of younger boys to follow them in their bird watching, tree naming, plant identifying, butterfly knowing, beetle picking, stone recognizing. And thus I escaped the clutches of the fair sex through those perilous years, thirteen to nineteen. Freckles do it. I became bewitched by the lovely elusive world of nature. And it has remained my love for more than sixty years.

But now I come to the point where I must tell the truth, the whole truth, and nothing but the truth, so help me!

I had fallen in love at the age of thirteen.

She was eleven.

To this day, I can show you the fire hydrant beside the Royal Conservatory of Music in Toronto where I dropped my four public library books and pretended to tie my shoe lace.

I watched them go by.

She was being dragged along by an older big blonde sister named Beth (as I later found out) but she was small and dark, with the most beautiful great eyes I ever saw or have ever seen. As she swept past, she looked at me. But she did not see me. (As I later found out.)

As a matter of fact, she did not see me for seven long years.

But, oh, I saw her.

They turned into Orde street, which was the first street down University avenue behind the Conservatory. Quick as a weasel, I snatched up my books and followed. Orde street is gone now, a blind street off University; tall skyscrapers loom. The old houses are all gone. But when I nipped around the corner, I saw the two of them scamper up the front steps of one house. And I could tell they were home.

I walked past the house. No. 6 Orde street. When I was safely out of its sight, I flew. Like a swallow, I flew up and along College street, up St. George, along Bloor street to the drug store of Mr. Norris at the corner of Howland. He was my friend. He also had a fat yellow book called a City Directory. Breathlessly, I told Mr. Norris of my need to know who lived at 6 Orde street. He was a perceptive man.

"Reverend James Murray," he said, looking in the Directory.

After a moment's reflection, and having no doubt been thirteen years old himself once, he then took the skimpy telephone book of that time and looked up Reverend James Murray.

"College 608," he said to central when she answered. (Though this was sixty years ago, I still remember that number.)

"Pardon me, ma'am," said Mr. Norris when someone answered. "But at what church does the Reverend Mr. Murray officiate? Erskine Presbyterian? Thank you."

And hung up.

"Erskine Presbyterian," Mr. Norris informed me with a smile I like to think I remember too.

Ah, well, from there on it is just the usual story. I had to go to Bloor street Presbyterian Church with my family at the morning service. But each Sunday evening, I was in the balcony of Erskine Church. This in time gave rise, by the time I was sixteen, to the general belief in my family and their friends that I was intending to enter the Presbyterian ministry. And they were all very pleased.

Year after year, every Sunday evening, I sat and watched. Oh, sometimes I would lose heart. Especially when, the moment the service ended, I would hastily skip down and mingle with the crowd that always gathered outside for a little while. And I would see her. She never saw me, I think now that if she had looked at me, I would have collapsed into a blob of jelly on the pavement. But what tormented me was that she grew more beautiful every year, far beyond my wildest reach of hope.

When I was seventeen or eighteen and started to Varsity, I was old enough to realize my folly, and for weeks I would not go to Erskine Church. But then, like a dog, I would creep back. Never had I heard her voice. So in my dreams I gave her a soft, contralto voice. Never had I seen her teeth, for she was a Presbyterian Murray who did not go about smiling in all directions. So I gave her beautiful white teeth. I gave her a character gentle, serene, compassionate. She was so perfect, by the time I was finished with her, that at the age of twenty, having had one last fearful look at her in the outpouring crowd of Erskine Church, I abandoned all hope, all dreams.

On the 17th of January, 1913, age twenty, I was a cub reporter on a newspaper. The University had thrown me out when I failed the first year twice, due to my devotion to the University newspaper, *The Varsity*. Each Friday, at 3 P.M., the staff of my new employers could draw their salaries. Mine was $12 a week. With this, around 4:30 in the afternoon, I would proceed to the Little Blue Tea Room on Yonge street, up a flight of stairs. There I would generously entertain my erstwhile Varsity friends to tea and cinnamon toast, or crumpets, or cocoa in winter. With about $3 I could play host in high style.

At 4:30 of January 17 I walked up the stairs and into the tea room. There were numbers of people sitting at the different tables. I headed for the alcove which was reserved for our Varsity party.

"Greg," said a young man whose name I have forgotten, rising to beckon me.

There was a girl with her back to me at his table.

"I'd like to introduce . . ." he began.

It was like being struck by lightning.

She smiled with the lips and teeth I had given her. At close range, she was more beautiful than I had painted her in my most magical dreams.

I took her home that afternoon. And no man ever took her home again. I was invited to supper. Reverend Mr. Murray, who was a tall, dark handsome man, looked at me with an expression I had long been familiar with in the passing brief glances of people. He told me long afterwards that on that first occasion he thought I was the dullest young man he had ever encountered.

I wasn't dull! I just wasn't THERE. I was in the Seventh Heaven, where no one speaks. The big blonde sister Beth whom first I had seen seven years before dragging my love along by the hand tried to monopolize the conversation at the supper table. But Mr. Murray and my love talked about fishing in Nova Scotia, and how the reverend gentleman had taught his little dark daughter to cast trout flies.

That was ONE thing I did not design for her. But when I heard about the trout fishing, I knew she was mine.

We were engaged six months later. We were married on the eve of the day before I sailed overseas to be absent from her two and a half years of war. For all but three years of half a century, we lived a joyous life, with only the one great tragedy when our first-born son was killed in battle in the second war. She died in my arms.

But you see I was possessed. That is why the fair sex have not bothered with me. They must sense when they see a man possessed.

Now why, you may ask, on this wintry night, do I tell so secret and idle a tale as this?

Well, on a wintry night such as this, the young, the ones on the threshold of life, are likely to be at home on a Saturday night. And on a Saturday, *Weekend Magazine* comes in. Maybe more often than at other times, the young, on the threshold of thirteen, fourteen, are more likely to come upon this story.

I tell you what you do, boy. Or girl.

Go and look at the western sky where the new moon, the silver shaving of the moon, hangs.

Look at it over your LEFT shoulder, and wish.

Wish that your first love shall be your last love.

And if your wish is granted, you will have put on the whole armour of life.

The Blister

My father never laid a hand on me; not in forty-five years. I was six years old before I knew fathers were allowed to spank little boys. This was the occasion on which my younger brother, aged three, Little Joe, committed his atrocity.

The street we lived on, McKenzie Crescent, was a very respectable neighbourhood consisting of tall, semi-detached residences that rented at eighteen dollars per month; which gives you some idea of their distinction. If one week's salary represented one month's rent, then the bank managers, executives, school principals and young newspaper editors like my father, Joseph Thomas Clark, were comfortably established in McKenzie Crescent.

But what lent real distinction to our street was the fact that Alexander Muir was our neighbour. He was the author of "The Maple Leaf Forever." He was, I clearly recollect, a tall man with a large, rugged, creative head who walked leaning forward as if into a high wind. We little children did not know why we should be hushed when he strode by. But we were told not to yell and lark about when Alexander Muir went by, daily.

We never found out who was responsible for Little Joe's atrocity. We are pretty sure it was either the Finch boys or the Calder boys. They attended Gladstone Avenue Public School, of which Mr. Muir was principal. They are the most likely villains.

Anyway, around 4:30 in the afternoon when Mr. Alexander Muir was leaning his way homeward, there was Little Joe, my baby brother, out on our lawn. And in his clear, beautiful voice he sang out:

"Old Daddy Man-ewer! Old Daddy Man-ewer!"

Mr. Muir chased him across the lawn and down our side entrance. (This was long years before side drives.) He caught Little Joe by the scruff and bundled him along the alleyway to the kitchen, where my young mother was starting to get dinner ready. She was a blushing woman.

Mr. Muir informed her of the outrage.

My mother suggested that a little child of three could hardly . . .

Surely some older children must have . . .

But in the eighteen-nineties, justice was justice, and no one was exempt. Mr. Muir instructed my mother to inform the child's father of the enormity.

I followed upstairs to the attic, where my mother got Little Joe in his nightgown and put him to bed to await the arrival of our father.

This put an end to an age-old tradition. It was traditional that Little Joe and I would be sitting on the top step at 5:30 P.M., watching. And when we saw Joseph Thomas come around the bend of the Crescent, with his newspapers under his arm and his walking stick swinging, we would jump and run to meet him, and as outriders, or equerries, escort him like a king proudly to his castle.

Instead, this night, I went up and sat at the foot of the attic stairs. I heard my father come home. I could hear the murmur of their voices as my mother told him of the atrocity. Then I heard him coming slowly up the stairs. In the dim gas-lit hall he saw me sitting on the bottom step. He halted in his tracks. In memory, it seems a long, long time he stood. Then he walked past me and up the stairs to spank Little Joe. I went down to the cupboard under the stairs on the ground floor, where they kept the extra leaves for the dining-room table.

Bella, the maid, rang the brass gong for dinner at 6:30

exactly. I can't remember how I got to the table. My eye-balls were made of lead. I could not raise them from my plate. My father and mother talked brightly of this and that, including me in their conversation. But my eyeballs were made of lead. Little Joe's place was unmade; there was neither plate, nor spoon. When the blancmange was eaten, and as soon as it was polite, I said: "Excuse me," and sidled from the table.

Little Joe was sprawled sound asleep on his bed. My young mother came up and pulled the sheet and the quilt over him and kissed me goodnight.

I did not cry. I don't remember ever crying. But I knew by the ache in my chest that a new dimension had come into the wide, wide world.

Breakfast was my father's favourite meal. He had played lacrosse in his youth and was now a cricket player, and was the Demon Bowler of the Parkdale Cricket Club. He was a small, lithe man, and he liked his breakfast. First, a bowl of oatmeal porridge (NOT rolled oats), with brown sugar and cream. Then two eggs with three strips of bacon. It was such bacon as has utterly been forgotten by man-kind. Its aroma, coming up the stairs in the morning, would EMBRACE you, as you hurried down. Two slices of tall, Gothic golden toast stood in the silver toast rack. Ah, you poor souls, you don't know what you have traded in for what you've got! Light, crisp, full of the savour of agriculture, fruit of the fields, this toast . . .

Little Joe always preceded me downstairs, because he had to be helped dress by his mother. As I came down, when Bella banged the gong at 8 A.M., I could hear my father and Little Joe in lively conversation at the table. My father was buttering Little Joe's toast.

But my eyeballs were still lead.

You would think nothing had happened. My mother and father talked gaily; Bella came in with a few cracks;

Little Joe appeared to have forgotten and forgiven all the past.

Just when Bella set the bacon and eggs before my father, I succeeded in raising my eyes to him.

Our eyes locked.

He shoved his chair back and stood up. He strode from the room; in the vestibule put on his hat and coat, and left.

Left his eggs and bacon, his golden Gothic toast, and the beautiful cherry jam made by our Grandma Greig, with one clove to each jar, exactly ONE clove, to dispense its magic throughout the jar of crisp, cool scarlet.

I looked in astonishment at my mother.

"You didn't do anything," she said.

That was the beginning. Like many writers, I pretend to a thing called total recall. But it is hard to recapture the ages, seven, eight, ten, in which a child becomes aware that there is something strange, unspoken, between himself and his father.

For example, he would be teaching me how to fish. He would be in the bow rowing seat. I would be in the stern, with the trolling rod held exactly right, a little below my left shoulder. Then something would happen. Maybe it would be only the beauty of the moment. Maybe the rock, the quiet water. Maybe a gull would sweep over, silent, beautiful. Or a song sparrow would sing unexpectedly from a bush. Our eyes would lock. My father would start to row faster. My bait would come to the surface. We would go back to the cottage. We would walk up the rocks. No explanation.

Or on winter nights, after supper, he would be reading to me something from the *Manchester Guardian Weekly*. It had a brown newsprint cover in those days. Maybe it was something by Scott, the great editor; or perhaps by C. E. Montague. He was my father's favourite. And when he was finished, our eyes would lock. He would snatch the paper down on his knees, and exclaim:

"Off to your homework!"

I think I knew by the age of ten that we were great friends; which is something more than the relation between father and son. Yet . . .

When I caught my mother in a young mood, I would try to explore the mystery.

"Sometimes," I would say to her, "sometimes, I have the feeling that my father doesn't . . ."

She would blush.

"Well," she would interrupt, "fathers often feel a little strange with their firstborn sons."

I was fourteen when I discovered the secret. It was my

grandmother, Louisa Greig, who revealed it.

By this time, I was at high school, taking not only Latin but GREEK. I had long pants. I was practically a man.

But I could not give up my childhood loves. And when, after school, I found Grandma Greig in the house, I would run and get the footstool, made of Turkey-red Brussels carpet, and set it at her feet. Then I would sit and get her feet between my knees, and away we would go, on the wings of her quiet recollection, into times past.

"Well," she said, on this occasion, "I wonder if you still have that scar on your butt?"

"Grandma!" I protested.

For, after all!

"Scar?" I said.

"On your backside," said Grandma Greig. "Did nobody ever tell you that story?"

I was born on the twenty-fifth of September, 1892. It was, according to Grandma Greig, a lovely long sunlit Sunday morning. The only heavenly body visible at the time was the sun. But all the planets, the constellations, were shaping themselves in the zodiac so that Virgo, the Virgin, was in the very act of handing over to Libra, the Scales, the destiny of anyone about to be born at this most propitious hour.

My young mother, Sarah Louise, was nineteen. She would not be twenty until Hallowe'en. And I was to weigh ten pounds, which is a pretty big job for a little girl of nineteen.

My mother being the baby of her family, naturally Grandma Greig was there in the upstairs front bedroom with Dr. Rae and his black beard. (I have his photograph.) In those days, everybody was born in the upstairs front bedroom. You went to hospital to die, not to be born.

All mother's sisters were there: Aunt Lil, Aunt Lib, Aunt Nan, fluttering in the hallways and spare rooms. Mamie Armour, the amateur astrologer and chum of my aunts, was there too; also Mrs. Taylor, from next door. And in the kitchen, Bella the maid kept all the cauldrons and preserving kettles boiling with pure water.

Mamie Armour put her head in the bedroom door.

"The child that is born at this hour," she called to Sarah Louise, "will have long life, prosperity, and countless friends."

"Where's Joe?" cried Sarah Louise.

Everybody knew where Joseph Thomas was. He was down the cellar, in the furnace room.

Nearly all furnaces, in those days, were hot-air furnaces. And a hot-air furnace was a monstrous erection, like a giant octapus, with great pipes leading off in all directions from its head. It being only September, of course, the furnace was not lit. Joseph Thomas had the furnace door open, with his head stuck in, listening to what could be heard down the pipes.

Ah, that worldly, sophisticated old man of twenty-six! He had much to listen to. Sarah Louise, with her mother and all her sisters for an audience, was making a good show of this great event.

Now, anybody who has ever stood over a hot-air registed will know that in hot-air furnaces, nothing is perfect. There is always a little leak. You can always catch a whiff of coal gas. And there was Joseph Thomas, smoking cigar after cigar on that eternal Sunday morning. Everybody knew where Joseph Thomas was.

From time to time, someone would come to the head of the cellar steps to call down the news. But Joseph Thomas, all his sins parading past him like a procession, wanted only the NEWS.

It was noon when at last I slid head first into this world.

"At high noon," said Grandma Greig. "At high tide."

"Tide?" said I.

"Well, anyway," said Grandma Greig.

Joseph Thomas became suddenly aware of a silence.

A stillness!

No more muffled cries down the furnace pipes. No more feet pitter-pattering overhead.

He stuck his head as far as he could into the furnace door.

Then he heard a child's cry.

OUT the furnace room, THROUGH the laundry, UP the cellar stairs.

"It's a BOY!" shouted Bella as he dashed through the kitchen.

Up the narrow back stairs – they all had narrow back stairs, in those days – he stumbled.

Along the hall, to where they were clustered at the door of the front bedroom. They made way for him.

On the bed, Sarah Louise, her face turned away on the damp pillow.

Dr. Rae, rolling down his sleeves.

On the rocking chair, Grandma Greig with a folded flannelette sheet, on which I lay, washed, tied off, ten pounds, purple.

Joseph Thomas stared around.

Grandma Greig lifted me on the sheet toward him.

He slid his hands under me, and burned my backside with his flaming cigar butt.

I leaped.

Grandma Greig snatched me back, rolled me over to see the scarlet blister already turning white.

"Well!" said Dr. Rae, starting to roll up his cuffs again. "What a way to welcome a fellow into this world!"

"Oh, God!" cried Joseph Thomas, throwing himself on his knees beside the bed and crushing one of Sarah Louise's hands against his face.

And that is the secret of the power I had over my father, all the joyous days of our lives.

The Napkin

The best way to go to hospital is all of a sudden.

If you have a month, or even a week, in which to prepare yourself, with the advice and help of your relatives and friends, you miss all the astonishment. The surprise.

No. All of a sudden, you wake up to find your family gathered around, staring down at you with expressions of unbelief. Your dear old family doctor, his hands held before him like some acolyte in a pagan rite, advances on you with the needle. He sticks it in your hip.

"What . . . uh. . . ?" you inquire dimly.

Next thing you know, two big young fellows, like police constables off duty, come smiling into your bedroom and pick you up like a trout. Lightly, they place you on a stretcher about the size of an ironing board.

And there you are, tilting down your very own front stairs, the pictures passing.

It is astonishing. It is the surprise of your life.

You go out your own front door feet first. You are slid into a gleaming white space capsule, and in an instant are whizzing through infinite space. One of those young fellows is in with you, sitting so he can look down at your face two feet away.

What the dickens was in that needle? Why, it is forty-seven years since you had that one shell-nose of army rum too many, to celebrate the victory of Vimy, or the slaughter of Passchendaele. This is fantastic. The pain, the aches that, like storm clouds in a summer thunderstorm, have been rolling and weaving, are subsiding. You think you can see enough blue to make a sailor a pair of pants.

You make one last effort to focus on the face of the young man bending above you.

"O.K., Pop?" he asks.

"O.K., lad," you say.

And that is the last thing you remember.

❦

I will now leave the second person plural and take up the first person singular.

When I woke, I was in a high, narrow white bed. It was four feet to the floor. The sheets were pure, trim, and they held me like straps.

It was a small pretty room. There were no pictures on the walls. At the foot of my bed stood a nurse. Forty, I think, though her hair was natural blonde.

She was a New Canadian. Polish. She had kind, but suspicious, eyes.

"You do not move," she said.

She held up an aluminum jug that looked like a cocktail shaker.

"You use this," she informed me firmly.

She came around and set the cocktail shaker on the little bedside table beside me.

"If you require more than this," she said, "you pull this cord. Do you see? I will pin it close to your hand."

She pinned the cord with a safety pin to my pillow.

"You pull this cord," she said, "and the orderly will come with the bed pan."

I was coming to.

I glanced around the tidy, clean little room, beige-coloured, with pretty curtains, a dresser and two chairs. Within six feet of me was as handy a little bathroom as you ever saw. It was handier, in fact, than many a bathroom I have met in hotel and motel.

I rolled my eyes to the bathroom and nodded.

"You do NOT move!" said the nurse.

I do not think she trusts Old Canadians.

"Take these," she said.

In a little shot glass, she gave me two beige-coloured capsules that matched the interior decoration. I downed them with a glass of water.

"NOT move!" she said.

And gave my bed a little pat.

❧

You waken always with surprise in hospital.

There is my doctor, and another doctor in a business suit; and three tall young doctors in long white coats. They strap my arm with the blood-pressure thing; listen to my chest with their little telephones, each doctor with a different touch, a different pressure. Very surprising.

A woman technician in a blue smock comes in pushing a sort of tea wagon. It has cables hanging off it like tentacles. She dabs my shins, wrists and chest with vaseline and straps the tentacles on to me. She presses buttons. The tea wagon purrs, whizzes, pops. Out of it threads a long film.

The doctors look at the film. They go over and murmur by the window. When they leave, the tallest, darkest, of the young fellows leaves last, reaches down and gives my big toe a tweak and gives me a wink.

I predict a great future for him in the practice of medicine.

❧

The blonde Polish nurse comes in.

"What day is it?" I ask her.

"Thursday," she says.

It can't be! Yesterday was Sunday.

That is the way time goes in hospital. You would suppose it dragged, weary hour after weary hour. No; time whirls.

"I have to wash your legs," says she.

"No, no!" I protest. "The student nurses washed me all over this morning."

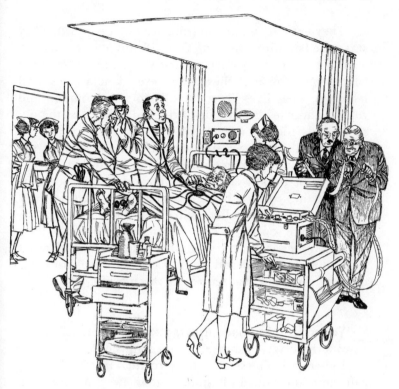

"This is this morning," says she, and proceeds to throw the covers off one side of me, while I duck.

She brings the basin and cloth.

But she really doesn't want to wash my legs. That is for the student nurses.

She just wants to see the bottom of my feet.

"Ah!" she says. "You have been OUT of bed!"

This is no reflection on the cleanliness of hospital floors. It doesn't take much dust to confirm the suspicions of a trained nurse.

"Just once," I admit.

"You do NOT move," said she.

Ah, they are astonishing.

They not only WASH you from head to toe in bed. They MAKE the bed with you IN it! You will just have to take my word for it. These young student nurses, all in starched white, who look as if they hadn't ever done a day's hard labour in their lives, let alone all morning, come in and roll you over to the far side of the bed. They toss the old sheets and bedding on top of you.

Then, slick as a whistle, they stretch and tuck in the fresh sheets and bedding on the free side of the bed.

With the utmost politeness and consideration for your modesty, they roll you back on to the freshmade side, draw the new sheets and bedding under you.

And there you are! It's all over in three minutes.

When they leave, carrying all the old bedding, they are as fresh and starched and smiling as if they had just come on parade, instead of at six o'clock this morning.

❧

Yes, sir. It is just one surprise after the other.

But there ARE, of course, certain confusions.

In her dark blue smock, the ward aid – that is what they call the housemaids in hospitals – took away my luncheon tray. My hand touched this paper napkin on the side of my bed. I drew it over.

Now, I am a connoisseur of paper napkins. I have watched their career from the beginning. I have no use for these measly arid little ten-inch things you pull out of those metal containers on lunch counters. For years I have been a big customer for what the pulp and paper industry later described as banquet-type paper napkins. Up at the cottage, you put them on top of the place mats in front of your small grandchildren. It takes a pretty athletic little boy to splash his soup beyond the fringe of a good big paper napkin.

But THIS napkin!

It was the most beautiful thing I had ever seen. I have with me at all times a measuring rule. It is the palm of my hand, for measuring trout. It is precisely seven inches from the tip of my middle finger to the first wrinkle of my wrist.

In rising excitement, I measured off the napkin.

Twenty-four inches! Square!

What a discovery!

No grandchild of mine could splash his soup THAT far.

Up at the cottage, it is a rule that when breakfast, lunch or dinner is over, all fold their paper napkins and hand them to the menfolk, who put them in their hip pockets. This is to wipe the gas and oil off the outboard motor. This is to dry off the dew from the skiff seat. This is to dry your hands after you have unhooked a fish. They have a hundred uses.

I picked up the phone and asked switchboard for head nurse at the desk on Four.

"Where," I said to her, "do you get the beautiful paper napkins? I just found it, after the girl had taken my tray . . ."

"Well, I can't tell you," said the head nurse. "But I can find out, if it's important."

"Important!" I cried. "Do you know, this thing is twenty-four inches square? Imagine up at the summer cottage, when you have all your little grandchildren squirting soup in all directions and . . ."

"Tell you what I'll do," said the head nurse. "I'll have you switched on to Miss Ketchin, the dietitian. She'll be the one to tell you."

I guess head nurses have some funny customers.

Miss Ketchin came on the line.

"Miss Ketchin," I said, "I want to congratulate you on the lovely meals we are getting. We've heard all those stories about hospital meals. Well, I, for one, would like to tell you . . ."

"You are very kind," said Miss Ketchin.

"What I REALLY am impressed by," I said, "are these

marvellous paper napkins you have. Where do you get them?"

"Yes," said Miss Ketchin, "we like to add little touches. I expect it is what they call a dinner napkin . . ."

"Miss Ketchin," I interrupted. "This is TWENTY-FOUR inches square! If you can imagine! Up at the cottage, we always have the men put the used napkins in their hip pockets, to wipe off the outboard engine, and wipe their hands when they have cleaned the fish and that sort of . . ."

"I'll drop up and have a look at it," said Miss Ketchin.

Excitement, I suppose, can convey itself even in hospitals, where everything is tuned to un-excitement.

Miss Ketchin came in. We exchanged pleasantries, and I repeated my congratulations on the attractive, small, inciting meals. Then I produced my napkin.

Miss Ketchin studied it, astonished. It isn't only the inmates of hospitals who can be astonished.

"This," she said, waving it about, "is not one of OURS."

We studied it together: its width, its breadth, its texture, its absorbency.

"My goodness!" said Miss Ketchin.

"Imagine," I said, "up at the cottage, when there's dew on the seats of the outboard in the morning . . ."

"I'll find OUT," said Miss Ketchin, taking my napkin away, after graceful farewells.

Miss Ketchin did not return.

In about twenty minutes, the floor head nurse came in my room. She was flaunting my napkin like a flag. She had that look of mischief and humour without which, I suppose, nobody can become a head nurse.

"This, Mr. Clark," she said, "is not a paper napkin."

"I beg your pardon?" I protested.

"It is what we call," said she, "a disposable bed-pan cover."

"A . . . uh . . .?" I checked.

"Disposable," she said, "bed-pan cover. You see the nurses hurrying along the corridor, with something hidden under one of these? This is a disposable bed-pan cover."

"My dear!" I said.

She handed me my paper napkin; gave my bed a pat, which is a secret sign all nurses have; and left.

Now, you think this is the end of the story. Before I left the hospital, I had got to know every nook and cranny of it – the superintendent, the purchasing agent. I got the source of my beautiful napkins. I got the name of a party who might be persuaded to sell, retail, what is intended only for hospitals.

O.K., boys.

This summer, my little grandsons can squirt it high, wide and handsome. All the menfolk will have bulging hip pockets; and no seat will be wet, no outboard disgraceful in its oil; no man's hands will smell of fish when he comes a-homing.

And when my distinguished visitors come to dine, on *truite amandine*, or on fillets of bass cooked to a recipe known only to myself and one other living descendant, and they are intrigued by the generosity of the Clark paper napkins, and they ask me where they come from . . .

I will tell them.

The Revolution

Our house was a man's house.

You could leave your tricycle in the vestibule, or on the front walk. Anywhere.

You could bring your tricycle in the front door, and with war whoops, ride it madly around the living room through the dining room, into the kitchen, and up the hall.

You could lean your hockey sticks up against the living room mantel, toss your baseball glove at random, throw your snow boots in winter here, there, anywhere.

It was a man's house.

There was Helen, my wife and their mother; Murray, aged eight, and Greg Junior, aged four. We had it the way we wanted it.

The slip covers on the chesterfield were khaki. And so was the one on the matching chair. The carpet was battle-proof. The drapes on the living-room windows were the manly type and could be accidentally torn down by charging buffaloes or Indians or cowboys.

We did a pretty good job of converting Helen into a man. We took her fishing, and she became so skilled with the bait-casting rod that she could outfish us all.

And the fly-rod! If we caught ten brook trout, with the young men using worms, Helen would catch seven of the ten. And all on the fly!

We had bought her a 20-gauge shotgun, to encourage her in the manly arts. With it, she would miss partridge in flight. The men and I – they armed with bows and arrows and imaginary guns, would yell: "Missed!"

And Helen, very proud, would call back: "I didn't want it, anyway."

In 1930, after a careful study of the catalogues, and several visits to sport shops, we decided that she was ready for a rifle. And we bought her, for her birthday on September 3, an 1894 Winchester carbine, calibre .25-.35.

Little did we know that it was the beginning of the end.

The Revolution had been born!

I took her off to the summer cottage in November, where we disported in the fine months. In the cottage, I detailed exactly where to hit a bounding deer, with diagrams. I organized some of the local boys to drive. I set Helen on a hill beyond the deserted golf links. Far off, I heard the cry of the drivers. (Of course, the younger men were not with us, due to circumstances beyond their control.) I heard four shots. I raced up the hill. There on a fallen log sat Helen, in tears.

"I missed!" she sobbed.

I patted her shoulder.

"You didn't shoot," I accused.

"The foreshoulder, every shot," she protested, standing up very manly.

Over the hill came Hugh Thompson, who operated the hotel in summer and was one of the drivers for the hunt.

"You got it!" he shouted. "A beautiful spike-horn buck."

Helen and I hurried to the far side of the hill, and there it lay. We helped gralloch it. Four shots. All in the foreshoulder. A running deer.

"It never knew," said Hugh Thompson, "what hit it."

It was the last thing Helen ever killed. We drove back to the city, and what an evening it was, in that man's house, as I related the tale. Helen sat back, quiet. She was four months pregnant.

November, December, the winter was celebrated as men celebrate, with slush tracked into the front hall, and clothes flung sideways, and lots of hoots and hollering, and gangs of fellow men invited in to play hockey on the hardwood floor of the living room (the rugs pushed aside).

It was late in March that the crisis came.

"The girls," announced Murray, "say you are going to have a baby!"

"Yes," said Helen.

"We'll call him," cried Murray, striking a dramatic posture, "George, after the King!"

"No!" shouted Greg Junior. "We'll call him Rutledge!"

"Rutledge?" said I.

"He's a friend of mine," said Greg.

"Oh, you mean Curly," said Helen.

"The girls," said Murray, standing back and surveying Helen in an intent fashion, "say he is in your stummick!"

"Yes," said Helen, relieved that things were going better than she had expected. We men had not particularly noticed her growing figure. There were many fat ladies in the neighbourhood at that time.

Greg Junior crawled up on the arm of her chair, carefully avoiding the bulge.

"How," he asked, "is he going to get out?"

"Through my mouth," said Helen.

"Oh," said Greg. "Like being sick!"

"Exactly," said Helen.

Greg climbed higher. With his two hands he pressed Helen's cheeks the way she did his when she wanted to put a spoonful of medicine in his mouth. Her mouth opened.

"Hello Curly!" shouted Greg Junior down the hatch.

That was near the end of March. On April 9 the Revolution began. Early in the morning. I did not wake the other men.

At noon, from the hospital, I called the house. Hilda, our young housekeeper, answered.

"What is it?" she cried.

"Ssshh! ' I pleaded, "Are the men home?"

"Murray!" called Hilda, already knowing.

"Dad?"

"You have," I announced, "a little sister!"

"A what?" he said.

"You have a *beautiful* little girl for your sister," I repeated proudly.

There was a dead silence. I heard the receiver bang down. I heard Murray say, in an undertone to Greg Junior . . .

"It's a girl!"

Well, I need not detain you with what happened to our house and home, a *Man's* house.

The first: The old pram that had done for the men was booted out and given to the Salvation Army. And in its place came a beautiful baby carriage, with lace and velvet, and sunshades and windshields.

The old crib was given to a neighbour; and in its place came the resplendent convertible crib-kiddie-coop, with curtains and frills.

But oh, far more important, came the rules.

No more yelling. No more hooting. No more leaving tricycles on the porch. In fact, you couldn't even come *in* the front door. You had to come around the *side* door. And no noise, you understand, gentlemen?

Tiptoe.

The whole house was transformed. Off came the good nut-brown slip covers from the chesterfield and matching chair. Flowered chintz appeared by magic, and you halted in surprise as you entered the living room. Down came the curtains, and up went gold-coloured curtains, which you were not allowed to grab hold of and pull aside to see what was going on outside.

And as little Elizabeth began to sit up in her carriage or crib and look at us, we were humbled. How big does a woman have to be to create a Revolution?

By autumn, no more hot dogs. No more hamburgers!

"We have," explained Helen, "to start to live like human beings."

Sirloin roasts of beef. Dressed pork tenderloin. Vegetables we, in our innocence, had never heard of in the days of hot dogs and hamburgers. Broccoli. Asparagus.

Scalloped potatoes! Nobody in the world could prepare them like Helen. As we sat stiffly at the dining room table, watching her, we realized she had been dreaming of cooking and preparing feasts for her men all the past years.

It seemed little Elizabeth had a great passion for bread dipped in the platter gravy of the roast beef.

"Some day," said Greg Junior, at last, "*some* day, *I'd* like to taste platter gravy!"

And that seemed to Murray and me the final article of capitulation.

Two women can beat three men, any old day of the week.

The Pinch

In fifty or one hundred years or so, a newspaperman makes a very large number of speaking acquaintances. Statesmen, tattoo artists; archbishops, prominent burglars; speed skaters, famous authors; all sorts of people in the news. They come, and they go.

To offset this haunting sense of the impermanence of things, a newspaperman generally cosies into a small, select company of his own choosing. Some of them go for golf or chess. They might take up collecting Canadiana, or shooting skeet. In my case, it was fishing, a thing you can follow from boyhood until you are old, old.

Commissioner George B. McClelland, of the Royal Canadian Mounted Police, was only a young inspector when I first encountered him. And though he is roughly twice my size and weight, we recognized each other on sight. We went fishing. I, of course, had risen through the years, to the eminence of fly fishing, a class who consider ourselves the élite of the angling fraternity. But George pointed out to me that pride is the sin against the Holy Ghost. He suggested that we go mudcat fishin'.

Commissioner McClelland and I in a canoe is quite a sight. I have to pile rocks under the bow deck of the canoe so that my paddle will reach the water. Mudcat fishin', you do not use a hook. With a darning needle, you thread a yard of fishworms on to a fishline. Then, hand over hand, you loop and knot the worms into a gob about the size of a golf ball. Then, at dusk, especially if there is a thunderstorm brewing, you head for the shallow bay, surfaced with water-lily pads, where the mudcats await you.

Between your knees you have a six-quart galvanized pail. Just as dark falls, you drop your ball of worms into the shallows. And when you feel the mudcat inhale your bob, you deftly, smoothly, draw him up, hold him suspended over the pail. Horrified, the mudcat, realizing he has left his native element, lets go and falls clank into the pail.

"Got one!" says George, in the dark. "Got another!"

In May and September, when the water is chill, even in the shallow mudcat bays, the mudcat is one of the finest of eating fish. Many a time, I have had my guides, who have paddled me all day in the beauty of trout stream and lake, take off after dark for some muddy pond to stock up with mudcats for breakfast. I could eat the trout.

Commissioner McClelland, of course, is a fly fisher, a bait caster, a spinner, and all the rest. But it is as a mudcat-fishin' companion that I hold him in highest esteem.

Among my other exclusive acquaintances was the late Captain Albin Dubé, conservation officer of the Department of Lands and Forests for a long stretch of the Georgian Bay. Captain Dubé had been a Great Lakes master before he accepted the job of conservation officer, which is the new-fangled title for game warden. They needed a ship master to command the diesel boat *Karanne*, forty-two feet, six inches, in which, with a crew of two, Captain Dubé put the law very kindly on that great sporting territory, Georgian Bay, with all its tricky reefs and shoals.

Captain Dubé never came into the little cove where my cottage is situated without heaving to, dropping anchor and, in the fast forty-horse-power outboard he towed behind *Karanne*, he would come in to see what I had been up to; and to sit, with a small, cold beer on my veranda for an hour or two of conversation about the wilds and about nature, in which he was richly versed.

He was just bidding me goodbye after one of these

visits when I suddenly recollected that George McClelland, by now an Assistant Commissioner of the R.C.M.P., had just the day before taken a cottage four miles north of mine at Wawataysee.

"Hey, by the way," I said to Albin, "how would you like to pay a little visit to an Assistant Commissioner of the R.C.M.P.?"

"Fine," said Captain Dubé.

"He's about as big as a moose," I warned the game warden. "And one of my favourite mudcat-fishin' friends.

"Suppose," I suggested, "suppose you drop in on him, and tell him you have a report that he has been trap-netting black bass?"

"Aha," said Albin.

"What's more," I warmed to the prospect, "tell him you have a report that his ice-box is full of black-bass fillets!"

"Oho," said Captain Dubé. "Where's his cottage?"

So we went indoors to my wall map where I pinpointed the cottage at Wawataysee in which Assistant Commissioner McClelland, with his wife Betty, and his three little daughters, had taken up residence far from the madding cares of Ottawa.

On the beautiful July afternoon, about 4, Mr. Assistant Commissioner, in nothing but his bathing trunks, is wading down by the cottage wharf trying to get the darned pipe primed, the pipe that feeds the water tank up the hill. Around him his little daughters in their bathing suits are disporting themselves. Betty is up organizing the cottage. (It takes a day or two to organize a Georgian Bay cottage at the start of the season, owing to the mice, flying squirrels, porcupines and other fauna of the region.)

Half a mile off, *Karanne* heaves to and casts anchor; and in a moment the fast little outboard is racing in. Captain Dubé, in his khaki uniform as conservation officer, is accompanied by one of his crew.

"Hi, there!" greets the Assistant Commissioner, always agreeable to men in uniform.

"McClelland the name?" inquires Captain Dubé, tying up to the dock.

"Yes."

"I'm Captain Dubé, conservation officer," said he. "I have a report that you have been trap-netting black bass."

"WHAT!" roared the Assistant Commissioner.

When he says "What," it sounds like a blast-off at Cape Kennedy.

"Furthermore," said Dubé, climbing out on the wharf, "I have a report that you have your ice-box full of black-bass fillets."

"Look here," cried the Assistant Commissioner, "we only arrived here last night! We haven't WET A LINE yet!"

"Sorry," said Captain Dubé. "But I have to investigate these reports."

"Now, just a minute!" declared the Assistant Commissioner, climbing out on to the wharf. "Do you know anything about me? Do you know who I am?"

"McClelland?" hazards Dubé.

"I," announced George, "am an Assistant Commissioner of the R.C.M.P. Am I likely to break your game laws?"

"Well, sir," said Dubé, "as an officer, you will understand I have to investigate these reports, even if they are unfounded."

He gestured up toward the cottage and started to walk thither.

"This," gritted the Assistant Comissioner, "is utterly ridiculous! Where did you get such reports?"

And George glared around at the distant neighbour cottages.

"Well, as an officer," said Captain Dubé, "you will understand I am not at liberty to reveal the source of information."

The girls were following up the rocks. They had never seen their Daddy in trouble before. Betty came out on the veranda, hands full of dusters.

"What goes on?" she asked.

"Why," cried George, "this is a game warden . . ."

"Conservation officer," corrected Captain Dubé.

"And he's got reports," said George, "that we've been trap-netting black bass, and our ice-box is full of bass fillets!"

"What nonsense!" announced Betty, barring the door.

She is a woman of spirit.

"He has to make a search," said George. "Let's go in."

They all went in, children and all, dripping.

Betty led to the kitchen.

"May I see the ice-box?" asked Captain Dubé, very correct.

George flung the ice-box door open.

This was something that hadn't ever happened to an Assistant Commissioner in the entire history of the R.C.M.P.

Captain Dubé squatted down and peered intently at the contents of the ice-box.

He reached in and picked a beer bottle – a nice, small, cold one.

Holding it aloft, he announced:

"With the compliments of Mr. Greg Clark!"

❧

Well, there was quite a scene.

Captain Dubé did not want to get north of Wawataysee until after dusk, where he had a special investigation to do. So he and his crewman helped George get the darned pipe and tank working. Then they sat on the veranda for an hour or two of conversation on subjects such as lawmen enjoy. And it was only because the other crewman aboard *Karanne* would have supper all ready that they didn't stay for supper.

When they left, the Assistant Commissioner went and stood for a long time, gazing out over the blue water and the grey and red rocks of Georgian Bay, thinking, figuring.

Daily, from Penetang, a small steamer comes up the shore, stopping at all the communities to deliver the mail and the provisions the cottagers have ordered from Penetang and Midland.

I do not usually go to the steamer wharf at our community. I let the children bring the mail and provisions.

"There's a registered parcel for you, Daddy," they said, "but we didn't have any money."

"Money?" said I.

"Yes, it was a registered, c.o.d. parcel. Two eighty-eight."

I hurried down to the wharf and took off in the outboard. I was too late. By the time I got to the community wharf, the post office was closed, and nearly everybody had gone with their cartons of provender.

I came home at slow speed. It is nice to think about what might be in a parcel. I have found that it is far more interesting to wonder what is in a parcel than to find out.

I spent a pleasant evening trying to think of anything that I had ordered. Maybe some new fishing lures? No. I had all of them. Who in the world would be sending me a gift, c.o.d., $2.88?

All next morning, I had to keep remembering to remind the children to bring home the registered c.o.d. parcel for me. But when 3 P.M. came around, boat time, I decided to go myself.

In fact, I got there ahead of the postmaster who, of course, is one of our community.

I paid him over the $2.88, signed the book.

He handed me out a neat, square, heavy little package.

I went around behind the post office and opened it with lively interest.

There were four books, and a small square piece of rock, just the size of a book.

The books were mouse-chewed, mildewed, warped, rain-stained, ancient.

On top was a letter.

Dear Greg –

Betty and I are so concerned for your health. We worry about you being bored. We hate to think of you sitting there with nothing much to do but think things up. So in the woodshed we found these rare old volumes which will help to occupy your leisure hours. The rock is the weight that fell from our hearts when Captain Dubé told us you were still alive and kicking.

Cordially, GEORGE

The books were:

The Ontario Royal Commission Report On The Dehorning Of Cattle (1898).

How To Take Pictures With Roll Film (1902).

The Catalogue For The Art Exhibit At The Canadian National Exhibition (1917).

Principles Of Mensuration (1890.)

❧

Two evenings later, just about an hour before mudcat-fishin' time, a speedy outboard with five aboard drew in to my dock.

I went down the rocks to greet it.

In the stern, the Assistant Commissioner.

He brought the skiff cautiously in. I stood alone on my dock. Five faces, looked at me.

"Even?" I asked, guardedly.

"Even," said the Assistant Commissioner.

Childish, eh?

No, SIR! The difference between speaking acquaintances and the few.

The Gregory Clark
Theory of Traffic

The Clark Theory of Traffic is so simple, so self evident, that I am astonished it was not thought of long ago.

In a nutshell, and I hesitate to use the word NUT shell, it is this:

Let everybody leave the car at home.

Let everybody use buses, street cars, taxis, suburban trains – and the traffic problem is solved in a mere twenty-four hours!

At first sight, this Theory may appear to be as preposterous in our time as did that of Nicolaus Copernicus (1473-1543). In his time Nicolaus suggested that the heavenly bodies did not revolve around the earth as the centre of the universe; but that the earth and the planets revolved around the sun. It was 215 years before his book was released from the Index Expurgatorius. I sure hope the Clark Theory doesn't get on the Index. But as a discontinuing Presbyterian, I don't suppose it would make much difference anyway.

The Clark Theory of Traffic is based on solid evidence, like that of Copernicus. Within 10 years, we won't be able to back our cars out of our side drives. Why? Because traffic on the street will be clogged solid, I refer, of course, to cities and towns and the highways between them. Oh, on dirt roads back in the country we may be able to get stretches of two-thirds of a mile or so for a little spin before we come–chug!–back into the immovable traffic again.

The Clark Theory is based on a principle not unlike Copernicus's. Up until his time, the whole world thought the earth was the centre of the universe. Until my time, the whole world thinks the automobile is an essential.

The motor car is a plaything. What the tricycle, the toy express cart or the roller skate is to little boys and girls, the automobile is to grown men and women.

A man gets up in the morning, shaves and dresses in haste, gulps his breakfast, all because his plaything is sitting there in the garage, ready to go. A woman who doesn't need a darn' thing at the grocery store or supermarket hustles through the dishes and the vacuuming and skins into her slacks so she can get in the plaything and go for a spin. No little child wakes up in the morning with more pleasurable excitement in the recollection of the tricycle out there on the back porch.

And all the time, the traffic grows and grows. But rather than face the facts, everybody still thinks the sun and planets revolve around the earth.

Of course, I am having a little difficulty with the Theory since it first occurred to me early in the fall. My family, for example, whenever I start coming around to the subject, even by the most roundabout and circuitous approach, suddenly hear the doorbell ring, or suddenly remember an urgent phone call they have to make. They even smell something boiling over in the kitchen.

As for my friends. Well, the four of us have had lunch together for I don't know how many years. But lately, they telephone that something has cropped up at the office.

I realize they have points to make with regard to the Theory.

"Think," protested my family, when I first got going, "how crowded the buses would be if everybody left the car at home!"

"How many taxicabs," my friends said, "would there have to be if everybody left the car at home?"

Things like that. Sheer evasion of the truth that the motor car, other than commercial vehicles, is a plaything. And the fun will soon be over.

I imagine Copernicus got into mixups like I did last Thursday.

Early in the spring, dear old J. B. McCoombe died, leaving behind the most beautiful collection of sporting gear any man ever possessed.

J. B. was one of our better-heeled sporting friends, and he was a perfectionist, not a collector. When he decided on a new rifle, or a new salmon rod, for example, he would dispose of his previous one to one of his rich but honest friends.

Cooper and I were pallbearers at his funeral and Herriot and Milne both came to the gathering at the house after the funeral. But that, of course, was no time to ask Mrs. McCoombe what she was going to do with J. B.'s lovely sporting goods.

There was, first of all, the custom built 7-mm. Magnum rifle with Circassian walnut stock, the very latest and most beautiful big-game job that J. B. had only used once, hunting in British Columbia, a year ago. It cost over $300, at least. The four-power scope probably cost another $90. And the tooled saddle-leather case for it, made in Texas, I bet cost a cool $100 more.

This was the item Cooper had his eye on. Then there was the dear little Belgian 20-guage over-and-under shotgun, selective single gold-plated trigger, raised ventilated rib, full choke and improved cylinder. With this, J. B. hunted grouse in Ontario, ducks in Saskatchewan, quail in Mississippi.

This was the apple of Herriot's eye.

We all knew that J. B. had got rid of his former salmon fly rods when he got this new one, from Britain, made by a Czech, a perfect beauty, 10 feet long, two joints with spare tip, and detachable butt. He had only used it the once, in Newfoundland in 1963.

That was what Milne wanted.

I wanted the trout fly rods. I knew that J. B. did not dispose of his previous fly rods. He probably had five or six of them. And among them was this little $2\frac{1}{2}$-ounce American rod, seven feet, a jewel, and not more than three fishing trips old.

"Why," Herriot would demand, at lunch, "don't you CALL Mrs. McCoombe and ASK her, plunk and plain, what she intends to do with these things?"

"Why don't YOU?" I would retort.

(This, of course, was before the Theory of Traffic had occurred to me.)

The McCoombes had no children. There were no dangerous nephews, as far as we knew. There was always the possibility that one of J. B.'s rich but honest friends might have quietly stepped in and skunked us. It was a pretty unnerving period, all the past spring and summer.

Then Thursday, the bell rang!

Mrs. McCoombe phoned Cooper.

"Frank," she said, "what am I going to do with all this junk of J. B's? The guns and stuff."

Junk! Stuff!

It took Cooper, so he says, ten seconds to catch his breath and clear his throat.

"Why, Mrs. McCoombe," he said, heartily, "I'll get some of J. B.'s old friends and we'll come and buy . . ."

"I was going to ask you," cut in Mrs. McCoombe, "for the name of some sporting-goods dealer or second-hand store that might . . ."

"No, no, NO!" cried Cooper. "You'd never get the true value. They'd offer you some ridiculous lump sum."

"Well, the reason I called you," said Mrs. McCoombe, "is that I'm off with Judith, my housekeeper, to Mexico for the winter tomorrow night. And it just occurred to me that a little extra cash might . . ."

"My dear Mrs. McCoombe," said Cooper. "When can I bring the boys?"

"Well, I'm tied up this afternoon with a farewell bridge party. Out for dinner. Tomorrow, I'll be crazy, packing."

"How," asked George, "about noon today?"

And inside of about six minutes, Cooper had the three of us on the phone.

We were to meet in Herriot's office at noon, and then proceed to Mrs. McCoombe's apartment uptown by 12:30.

"She's going to have Judith fix up some sandwiches and coffee," said Cooper.

❧

It was an enthusiastic gathering at Herriot's office, especially for me, as I hadn't seen too much of the boys these past three or four weeks.

"Now," said Cooper, rubbing his palms together, "let's agree beforehand, so there won't be any embarrassment at Mrs. McCoombe's. I think you are all agreed I get the rifle. I figure on giving her $100 for it."

He glanced around to see how we felt as to that.

"Well," I suggested, "after all, that rifle, with the scope, and that hand-tooled leather . . ."

"O.K.," said Cooper briskly. "One hundred and twenty-five dollars. How does that sound?"

"I take the shotgun," said Herriot. "And since he has used it quite a bit, maybe $75?"

"Make it $100," said Cooper. "After all, that little gun, with the single selective trigger and all must have cost $350 new."

"Right," said Herriot. "A hundred dollars."

Milne thought $75 or so for the salmon rod was about right, and my suggestion that I take the bunch of trout fly rods for $75 was O.K.

"Except, of course, the reels," said Cooper. "J. B. never bought a fly reel under $25 in his life. And they'll all have double-tapered lines, at $12 to $15 . . ."

"They won't be new," I pointed out. "But O.K. Ninety dollars for the lot."

Cooper glanced at his watch.

"O.K., let's go!"

"My car's down in the parking lot," said Herriot.

I pointed to the window.

It was pouring and sleeting, a slashing spectacle.

"Your car," I said, "is in the parking lot how far along?"

"Just a block and a half," said Herriot, getting into his coat.

"Now look here, boys," I reasoned. "We don't know exactly where Mrs. McCoombe's apartment house is. Maybe there is no parking within half a block. Let us take a taxi."

"My car . . ." began Herriot.

Then he caught a glance from Cooper and Milne, which I did not fail to see.

"This is a LOGICAL occasion," I said, "on which to take a taxi. I . . . uh . . ."

"O.K., O.K., O.K.," they all said; and Herriot called his secretary to ring for a taxi. We took the elevator down to the lobby, and by the time we got there, the cab was at the front door.

"See?" I said, calmly, as we ducked out through the sleet and into the cab. I got in front beside the driver. The others crowded into the back seat.

"I'll look after the cab fare," I said, "and we'll settle later."

As we sloshed and swerved out of the downtown area, I hoped they realized the sensibleness of the Theory.

"Now, once more," said Cooper, in back. "Let's get it all clear. I give her $125 for the rifle. Herriot, you $100 for the 20-gauge. Milne you, $75 for the salmon rod. And Greg, you $90 for the trout rods."

"Right!" we all said.

"That comes to $390," said Cooper, "which is better than she would have got from any dealer. Or from any of J. B.'s rich but honest friends. They'd have handed her $200 for the lot."

We nipped out of the downtown muddle and took a street I never realized was there. And after a few more twists and turns at a smart pace, we drew up in front of a large, fashionable apartment house.

"Here we are," said the taxi driver.

He got out and opened the door for the others. I looked at the meter – $1.70.

The boys ducked in to the apartment lobby while I paid off the driver. I gave him $2. He gave me back thirty cents. I gave him twenty.

When I headed for the door, the taxi driver came in with me.

In the lobby, Cooper had found Mrs. McCoombe's number and rung the signal bell. The taxi driver came with us down the hall.

"We'll call a cab," I said, "when we want one."

"That's o.k.," said the taxi driver comfortably.

He was a stout, middle-aged fellow.

"Now, just a minute," I explained to him. "This is a . . ."

"That's o.k., bub," he said, "I got lots of time."

Judith had the door open down the hall, and Mrs. Mc-Coombe was waiting just inside to greet us.

"This is wonderful of you boys," she said, shaking our hands. "Just hang your coats in the closet here."

"This," I said, "is the taxi driver."

For he had come in too.

"Fine, fine!" said Mrs. McCoombe. "I've got everything laid out on the dining-room table. We can go right to work, because the bridge girls are coming at two o'clock on the dot."

There they were. The beautiful custom-job rifle, lying on its leather scabbard, the scope in place, all shiny just as J. B. must have left it so carefully. And the shotgun in its rich square leather gun case like a large despatch box. And the rods laid out on their cloth bags, the aluminum rod cases beside them, the reels in their leather bags.

The taxi driver had sat down on a dining-room chair, twiddling his cap round and round on his thumbs.

"Well, Mrs. McCoombe," began Cooper, picking up the rifle lovingly. "We're happy to have this opportunity of getting such wonderful remembrances of J. B. We've talked it over, and I have chosen the rifle. I will give you $125 for it."

"A hundred and fifty dollars," said the taxi driver.

We froze.

"A hundred," said Cooper, very distinctly, "and SEV-ENTY-FIVE!"

"That's a mighty valuable weapon," said the taxi driver, still twiddling his cap. "I do quite a bit of hunting myself. A hundred and ninety."

"Mercy!" said Mrs. McCoombe.

"TWO," said Cooper more loudly than he needed, "HUNDRED!"

"You got it," said the taxi driver.

"Mercy!" repeated Mrs. McCoombe. "I had no IDEA these things cost so much. J. B. never used to tell me the cost of . . ."

Herriot reached in and picked up the butt and barrels of the little shotgun from the leather case and fitted them together. Then he put the forend on and swung it at imaginary passing birds.

"I'll be mighty proud, Mrs. McCoombe," he said, "to own this souvenir of dear old J. B. I offer you $100 for it."

"A hundred and twenty-five," said the taxi driver, calmly.

I thought for a moment that Herriot was going to swing the gun on him. Then he gave me a curious look. A little bitter.

"A hundred and fifty," said Herriot.

"A hundred and sixty," said the taxi driver.

"A hundred," enunciated Herriot through his teeth, "and NINETY dollars!"

"You got it," said the taxi driver.

With trembling hands, Herriot took the gun down and

placed it back in the handsome brown box.

The taxi driver ran Milne up to $95 for the salmon rod and reel; and for my five rods, including the beautiful little 2½-ounce American jewel, he ran me up to $135.

"Some of my pals," he apologized, "are always on the lookout for a nice little fly rod."

"Mercy!" said Mrs. McCoombe. "I had no IDEA! I thought I might get $50 or something for all this. A little loose cash to take to Mexico. But HEAVENS!"

❧

At this moment, Judith appeared, pushing one tea wagon ahead of her, and pulling another behind her. They were loaded with the most delicious little sandwiches and cakes. In the middle of the front tea wagon was a big silver dish heaped with smoked salmon sliced as thin as razor blades.

"It's SCOTCH smoked salmon," said Mrs. McCoombe. "J. B. always loved it. Those little brown sandwiches are filled with REAL Caerphilly cheese from Wales. And that white cheese is Feta, from Bulgaria – comes in brine, very salty, tangy. J. B. loved it too."

Well, that taxi driver, putting his cap on the floor, ate a quarter of the smoked salmon. There were six of us, counting Mrs. McCoombe, but I bet he ate two-thirds of the Caerphilly sandwiches, and pretty near half the big square lump of Feta.

Among the cakes was a pile of those little chocolate éclairs about the size of a golf ball. He ate five of them.

"Well, gentlemen," said Mrs. McCoombe, looking at the sheaf of cheques we had written out on the buffet, "this is wonderful. I don't know how to thank you."

"Not-atall, not-atall!" said the taxi driver, belching briefly and picking up his cap.

"Aw, you poor MAN!" cried Mrs. McCoombe. "You didn't get ANYTHING!"

She put her hand to her cheek and thought.

"Judith!" she called suddenly. "Where's that tent?"

Tent!

Holy mackerel!

Surely this wouldn't be the tent J. B. had brought from Scotland last winter, just a month before he died. He had showed it off to us soon after it arrived. Holds four persons. Fits into a little silk bag no bigger than a sofa cushion. The telescoping aluminum poles fitted into another little silk bag about the size of a stick of French bread. The whole thing, counting duty, came to over $175.

In came Judith with the tent.

It WAS the tent.

Mrs. McCoombe took it and plumped it, both bags, into the arms of the taxi driver.

"There!" she said. "You won't have to go away empty-handed. Now, gentlemen, the girls will be here in forty minutes and I have to change."

And, thanking us profusely, she showed us and our loot out the door.

It was still raining pitchforks and sleeting. We ducked into the waiting taxi.

I got in beside the driver again. He put the tent between us on the seat, and we rested our elbows on it.

Nobody spoke all the way back to Herriot's office.

With their loot, the others got out and ducked into the lobby.

"One," I checked, "seventy."

"Correct," said the taxi driver.

I handed him $2. I waited for the 30 cents. I took it all. He shrugged.

"I didn't charge anything," he reminded, "for waiting."

I gave him a look.

He never batted an eye. Just reached over and slammed the cab door and drove off.

When I got into the lobby, the others had already gone up in the elevator.

On entering Herriot's office, the three of them were

sitting looking in different directions. I could tell they had just been talking about me.

"The taxi," I said, "came to $3.60. That's 90 cents each."

They dug down.

"I . . . uh . . ." I said, "didn't tip him for the return trip."

Nobody said anything.

"Well," I said, cheerily, my rods in a bundle under my arm, "I guess I'll be running along."

Nobody said anything.

So I ran along.

It will be some time before I can talk about the Clark Theory of Traffic in certain areas of my acquaintance.

Maybe I can discuss it now and then with strangers sitting beside me in buses.

The Man With
the Honest Face

The bus was jammed.

Those of us home-goers standing in the aisle were so squashed together that when the bus braked suddenly, and we were lurched against one another, I did not at first notice the scuffle going on right next to me.

Then I saw that the man second ahead of me, a big man in his forties, was holding aloft the arm and hand of the elderly man immediately next to me.

"Lady!" he was shouting to the woman sitting in the seat beside us. "Pick up my wallet, will you? I got my foot on it. There's $83 in it!"

Still holding the old gentleman's arm and hand high, he gave him a shove against me, so as to make room on the bus floor.

The lady reached down. I saw the foot of the large man lift. And the lady picked up the brown scuffed wallet.

"Hang on to it, lady!" commanded the big fellow. "DRIVER! DRIVER!"

The bus slowed, and the driver answered.

"Driver," yelled the big man. "I got a pickpocket here! Stop at the next policeman you see, will you?"

We passengers were stunned. The bus accelerated.

None of us was more stunned than I. For I had noticed the old man particularly in the few blocks we had run. He was soberly clothed, and had a small white beard. We had smiled at each other apologetically as we were forced to squash against each other.

I supposed he was probably a retired clergyman. Or

perhaps an old pensioner of one of the downtown commercial offices, homeward bound after a visit with his old colleagues. His clothes had that neat and slightly worn look of the retired.

And there he stood, an old man, in a grotesque attitude, the big man firmly holding his left hand and arm straight toward the bus ceiling.

He turned an agonized face to me. Tears were flowing.

"Oh, please," he said. "It's all a mistake! When the bus jerked like that, I fell against him and naturally grabbed for support . . ."

"Ya!" cried the big fellow. "And grabbed my wallet!"

"Now, look," I put in, taking a supporting grip on the old man's free arm. "That's QUITE possible. When we lurched like that. The natural thing is for the hand to close on whatever . . ."

"Yah?" said the big fellow, staring at me coldly. "And how did he get my coat tails up? You keep out of this, mister."

One more look at the tragic face of the old man turned to me, and I would be darned if I would keep out of it.

Suddenly the bus stopped. We could hear the driver calling to someone out the front door. And in came a tall policeman. After a brief chat with the driver, the policeman pushed his way amidst the packed passengers.

I made way for him.

"Now what have we here?" he asked calmly.

"I felt this old bird's hand in my hip pocket," stated the big fellow. "I made a quick grab, and caught his hand with my wallet in it. He dropped it on the floor there. And that lady picked it up. She's got it now. There's $83 in it!"

"Officer," I announced, and I could sense a good deal of friendly support from those right around us, "the bus stopped suddenly. We were all flung against one another. This old gentleman, next ahead of me, half fell against this other gentleman . . ."

"Wauff!" cried the big man. "I caught his hand right IN my hip pocket! And my wallet in his hand. And there's $83 in it."

He had let go the old man's arm. Clutching his lapels around his neck, the old man was the picture of abject terror.

"Constable," he said in a trembling voice, "the bus gave a lurch. I fell against this gentleman. You know how the hand automatically clutches against anything . . .?"

The constable was one of those thirty- to forty-year-old members of the force who don't try to be judge and jury.

"Driver," he called, the bus still being stationary. "Go ahead to the next stop light. I've got a phone there."

He put a kindly and protective hand on the old man's shoulder.

"We'll just call the squad car," he said, "and we'll go to the station and clear this little matter up. Lady, would you be kind enough to come along? Sorry to delay you. But you picked the wallet up?"

She handed the wallet to the constable and gathered her purse and a couple of parcels.

"Do you require me?" I demanded.

"Are you acquainted with this gentleman?" asked the policeman.

"I never saw him before in my life," I said. "But I know an innocent man when I see one, and . . ."

"Did you see any of the activities mentioned by this other man? Did you see the wallet in his hand?"

"No, but I can testify that the bus lurched and . . ."

"I think we have enough evidence as to that," said the constable.

The bus drew to a stop. We all stood aside as the constable, with his friendly supporting hand on the old gentleman's upper arm, and the lady and the big fellow, were let out the side door of the bus.

I felt snubbed. I turned and studied the faces of those pressing around, those seated immediately by.

"Look," I said, "would any of you care to give me your names and addresses? I intend to follow this up. That benevolent old gentleman, accused of being a PICKPOCKET! And it is so perfectly obvious that when you are flung against somebody, you NATURALLY grab . . ."

Nobody was looking at me. I lost that sense of association that I was conscious of a moment before.

"You, sir," I said, to the man who had been sitting against the window beside the woman who picked up the wallet.

"I don't want to get mixed up in this," he said briefly. "I didn't see anything."

"You, sir!" I said to a big, young, blond man who had been squashed next beyond the accuser.

"You get mixed up in a thing like this," he said, "and you spend half your time sitting around police courts . . ."

"Ladies?" I protested, looking around at the women jammed in.

They were looking into their purses, or staring up at the ads along the ceiling of the bus.

I subsided into indignant silence. When my bus stop came, I got off and walked home. I did not enjoy my dinner. I could not forget the terror of that kindly old man. After dinner I thought, an old man myself, of all the perils. Suppose I was flung against somebody in a bus? Suppose I made a clutch that landed on a woman's handbag? Or worse, if it landed on some part of the anatomy of a young lady?

At 8 P.M., I telephoned police headquarters and described to the switchboard girl the location of the incident. She put me through to the district police station. A desk sergeant answered, and I explained my interest.

"A decent old gentleman,' 'I said, "with a small white

beard, charged with picking pockets. I was on the bus . . ."

"Just a minute," said the sergeant. "I'll connect you with the detectives in charge of that."

A quiet voice asked me:

"Do you know the man?"

I explained how I knew an innocent man when I saw one, and that the circumstances . . .

"You can appear, if you like, at the Police Court tomorrow morning," said the detective kindly, "at 10 A.M."

"But how about his family, his friends?" I asked.

"As far as we can find out," said the detective, "he has no family, and no friends in particular. He lives in a rooming house down on Parliament street."

"Aw," I put in.

"So if you care to be present in court tomorrow morning . . .?"

"Is he in the cells? How about bail?" I inquired.

"No bail," said the detective.

"No BAIL!" I protested.

"I'm sorry, sir, this is all the information I can give you."

I went to bed. My dreams were troubled. Full of lightly-bearded old men with sad eyes and trembling mouths.

At 9:30 A.M. I was at the Police Court. Being an old reporter, I knew the ropes. I got the door constable to let me speak to the clerk of the court. He pointed out the detective handling the case.

"I spoke to you on the phone last night," I said to him. "I was right beside him . . ."

"Ah, yes," said the detective. "If you'll sit in the spectators' benches over there, we'll call you."

It is a good thing for us all to spend a day of the year in the Police Court, watching the quiet, brief processes of the law; the tragic procession of our fellow beings involved in the most extraordinary toils; the tall, quiet cops.

Ten cases were called before my old friend with the

white beard came up from below and stood in the cage-like prisoner's dock.

His back was to me. I could not signal him, to let him know I was there, that there was compassion in his world.

The first witness was the big fellow who had held the old man's arm aloft, and who had laid the charge.

❧

He described in minute detail the whole incident. Fairly, without passion, except when he said his wallet had contained $83.

The woman witness was next. She related, hesitantly, how she had been called upon to look at the bus floor and see the man's foot move, revealing the wallet. And she had picked it up, as requested.

"Do you wish to take the stand?" asked the magistrate.

I was thunderstruck to see the old white head shake in refusal.

I was on the point of rising to my feet.

The crown attorney rose, with a foolscap sheet in his hand.

"Your Worship," he said, "I might say our pick-pocket detail chased this man out of town last August, during the Exhibition. Here is his record, dating back to 1938. In 1938, in Seattle, two years. In 1941, in Pittsburgh, four years. In 1946, in New York City, two years. In 1951, in San Francisco four years. In 1959, in Toledo, Ohio, two years. In 1962, in Richmond, Virginia, two years."

"All for picking pockets?" enquired His Worship.

"Yes, Your Worship," said the crown attorney.

"A travelling man," said His Worship.

I sat transfixed, my eyes on that old venerable head.

"Remanded a week," said His Worship, "while we consider the possibility of his being an habitual criminal."

The old man turned to go down the stairs from the dock.

I waved; but he did not see me.

I edged along the spectators' benches and made for the door.

The detective followed me into the corridor. He put his arm kindly around my shoulder.

"Pop," he said, "I'm sorry. But you can't tell by the looks."

"Thanks, lad," I said.

And went about my business.

The Baby at
Rat Dam Lake

Alex Hennessy is a bush pilot. He and his brothers have been for many years engaged in the art of transportation in the less accessible areas of Northern Quebec and Ontario. They have lifted some mighty loads in the mine, lumber and construction activities of the frontier. Their business slogan is "We move anything anywhere."

The strangest thing they ever moved was a baby weighing two pounds four ounces.

Alex Hennessy was based at Sioux Lookout, Ontario, his aircraft being a single-engine Beechcraft, a five-passenger plane on skis.

Based on Sioux Lookout also is Gifford Swartman, Indian agent (they call them superintendents now) for a wide expanse of territory including parts of both Ontario and Manitoba. He has 6,600 Indians on his hands and mind. If you happen to mention Gifford Swartman's name to an Indian anywhere from Quebec to the Queen Charlotte Islands, that Indian's eyes will light up. Indians have heard of him.

One sharp, gray, winter day, Swartman called Alex Hennessy:

"An Indian woman," he said, "pretty sick, at Rat Dam Lake. Know where that is?"

"About sixty miles this way from Bearskin Lake," calculated Alex.

Sioux Lookout is pretty far up, to start with: northwest of the top of Lake Superior. Away to the northeast, across the wide watershed of the Albany, which flows into James Bay, is the Severn, which flows into Hudson Bay.

Bearskin Lake is one of the myriad lakes that lie in the flat, featureless and moonlike country that is drained by the Severn. On it is a minor Hudson's Bay Company post. Sixty miles "this way" of Bearskin is Rat Dam Lake. On foot from Rat Dam had come the word to Bearskin that an Indian woman was pretty sick.

And over the grapevine of those little generator radio sending sets that the Hudson's Bay Company and the federal Department of Transport operate, a spiderweb of communications in that last lone land, Bearskin post sent the word to Gifford Swartman.

Gifford told Alex Hennessy to go and get her.

"What's her name?" checked Alex, pulling on his mitts.

"Chapman," said Swartman.

As if her name mattered.

From Sioux Lookout airfield, where he kept his Beechcraft, Alex took off into the winter gray. To you and me, it will forever remain a mystery how bush pilots find their way across those motionless jigsaw immensities of the northern world. To them, it is nothing.

It is 325 air miles to Bearskin from Sioux Lookout, a couple of lonely, watchful hours for Hennessy there in the front of his craft, peering, checking, thinking. Thinking, maybe, that this is something around $270 – two hundred and seventy bucks, that is, out loud. To go in and find a sick Indian woman. Pretty sick.

In due time, Alex came out into the sub-Arctic moors of the Severn headwaters. In a matter of minutes, he saw the distant shape of Bearskin Lake. On his map, he checked for Rat Dam.

Rat Dam Lake is just another of the treeless, bushless expanses of iron ice and white snow that show where lakes lie in winter. It is the shape that tells.

Down to good observation height, Alex lowered the

Beechcraft. Around the lake he went in a throttled down circuit.

Now, in all that country, you don't see a living soul for hours of miles. What Indians there are in it are in single families. It would be a single family, Alex figured. He made the circuit of Rat Dam without the slightest sign of life. No smoke, no tracks in the snow, no cabin, no tent.

Well, now, this was a fine pickle. That $270 – out loud, that two hundred and seventy bucks! – and go back and tell Gifford Swartman he couldn't find anybody?

Alex thought he might fly on to Bearskin and land at the post to make inquiries. But at the same time, flying low anyway, he dropped to about twenty feet and flew the length of Rat Dam Lake, watching the shores.

Then he saw a telltale sign. It was a slight hump in the snow, close up to shore. To a bush pilot, this indicated a waterhole the Indians dig and wall around with heaped-up snow to keep the cold wind off it. But this hole was drifted in. Just the lump.

Alex landed. He taxied toward the waterhole. And down an untrodden path from the spruce and scrub came an Indian.

Alex climbed out of the plane and waded toward the Indian.

"Got a sick woman here?" asked Alex.

The Indian nodded, and motioned him to follow.

Up the snowed-in path, Alex followed. The Indian led him to a tent. Its walls had some low logs for shelter. It was floored with logs. It was, however, only an old tent.

The Indian, speechless, pointed to a low bed which was entirely covered over with one of those gray-white rabbit skin blankets the Crees make: a quilt made of scores of rabbit skins, strung together and woven into a wonderfully warm comforter.

Alex leaned down and drew back the robe. The Indian woman was there, cold and dead.

"Chapman?" asked Alex, replacing the quilt.

The Indian nodded.

"How long?" asked Alex. "How long dead?"

The Indian held up two fingers.

"Two days?"

The Indian nodded. He never spoke throughout the story.

"Sorry," said Alex. "Swartman. Swartman send me. To pick up sick woman. You understand?"

The Indian looked down at the covered bed.

"Too late," said Alex, bending to go out the tent flap.

❧

The Indian took Alex's sleeve.

He pointed over to another corner of the tent, where there was a small cardboard carton, the kind a dozen cans come in. It, too, was covered with a rabbit skin quilt, a very small one.

Alex supposed the Indian meant that he was out of food. But the Indian plucked Alex's sleeve again, and motioned him toward the small box.

Alex Hennessy lifted the rabbit skin. And there, bedded on another layer of rabbit skins, lay the smallest baby he had ever seen or imagined in his life.

It had not even been washed since birth. Alex, after an astounded glance at the Indian, reached in and touched the incredible morsel.

It was warm. It was alive.

Alex carefully replaced the small rabbit skin coverlet and stood up. He and the Indian stared at each other a long moment.

"How far to Bearskin?" he asked.

The Indian shook his head.

"What have you got to feed it?" demanded Alex, in sign language.

The Indian pointed to a pail of water; to a pot containing some monstrous stew or other.

"No milk?" suggested Alex, a little frantically.

But he didn't wait for the Indian to reply. He reached over to the bed. He drew the big rabbit skin off the body of the dead mother. He laid it on the tent floor. Then he took the small box and spread its small rabbit skin coverlet on top of the large one.

More scared, he says, than he has ever been in his life, Alex reached in with his cold hands and lifted that tragic little unwashed mite, its eyes crusted, its miniature limbs shuddering from his touch, and placed it on the rabbit skins.

While the Indian stood above him watching, Alex began folding the rabbit skins around the baby, building up a sort of funnel of the fur through which it might breathe. He was not sure whether it was breathing or not. All he knew was that it was warm, and that it moved feebly.

Alex waded down the trail toward the plane. The Indian at his heels. When he reached the ice and the Beechcraft, the Indian seized Alex's arm. Alex shook the Indian off and opened the aircraft door. He set the big soft fur bundle on the seat beside his own. From the far side, he climbed in. The Indian followed, hopeless, around after him.

He started up. He taxied away. From far down Rat Dam, he could see the Indian standing in the snow.

He feels, in a way, that he decided. But at the same time, he says it felt a little as if something else were deciding for him, all that two or three minutes it took him to wrap the baby up and carry it off. It may have been simply the humanity that is back of all men's lives, for generations, that went automatic in him, and activated him.

For when he got straightened out for Sioux Lookout, Alex began to feel what a crazy thing he was doing. He had been sent in to bring out a sick woman. And here he was stealing a baby that might already be dying, might now be dead here in the plane seat beside him, or certainly might

be dead, up in this cold, before he could get it into safe
hands.

"Meanest trip of my life," says Alex Hennessy today.

❦

And it was two hours and something long. It was growing
dark when he slid down on Sioux Lookout. He drove his
car over, and quickly transferred the rabbit skin bundle
from plane to car.

There is a small Red Cross hospital in Sioux Lookout.
It does a lot of railroad and similar business.

The matron was in the front hall when Alex pushed
through the door with his rabbit skin bundle.

"What have you got there?" she cried, in alarm.

Alex set his bundle down.

"It's a baby," he said. "The mother is dead. It's terribly
small. It's only about that long . . ."

"But good heavens!" the nurse protested. "We haven't
got any equipment. Don't leave it here, take it to Kenora,
Sudbury, a big hospital . . .!"

Alex Hennessy was too happy to see a woman, a hospital, anything, to consider beyond this instant.

"It may," he said, "be dead now."

And he walked quickly out the door.

He went first to the restaurant for a cup of coffee. As he
approached the restaurant, he saw Gifford Swartman across
the street.

"Hey! Giff!"

Swartman came over, and Alex led him into a booth.
He gave Swartman that long look a man uses to indicate
that he is about to unload.

"The woman," he said, "was dead."

"Ah, too bad."

"But there was a baby," said Alex. "I brought it. It is
about that long. It is the littlest, smallest, most measly . . ."

"Premature, maybe?" asked Swartman.

"The mother," said Alex, "had been dead two days. But it was warm. A little. It moved. So I brought it."

"Good," said Swartman.

"It may be dead now," said Alex, thinking of that rabbit skin heap, and the funnel he made up through it.

They drank their coffee.

❧

The telephone in the cafe rang. A waitress answered.

"It's the matron from the hospital, Alex," called the waitress. "What's the baby's name?"

"Chapman," called Swartman, instead.

"Chapman," said the waitress. "The nurse wants to know its other name."

"Is it a boy," called Swartman, "or a girl?"

The waitress asked.

"It's a boy," she replied.

Swartman, the one the Indians like, and white men too, took a look at Alex there, all relaxed.

"His name," called Swartman to the waitress, "is Hugh Alexander."

That is Alex's name.

Well, that miniature baby was not dead. And the Sioux Lookout hospital that was so startled to have it dumped in its lap, was, inside a week, bewitched by it.

And it grew, and it throve. And in a couple of months it was the apple of a dozen people's eyes, including Swartman, Alex, the nurses and sundry others.

And slowly, across that spiderweb of radio from the Department of Transport and the Hudson's Bay Co., the word of him reached away back into Bearskin and Rat Dam; and in due time came the message back that the baby's aunt would like to adopt it. That's the way the Indians are. They don't trust us with their babies.

So, at about six months, Hugh Alexander Chapman, a beautiful boy, with that ivory color and that quality of

Chinese art which an Indian child has about him, was made ready to go back unto his people.

Alex Hennessy bought him a complete layette.

The matron and nurses rigged him out with dresses, coatees, bootees, bonnets, sweaters, soakers, bibs and tuckers.

And on a fine fall day, Hugh Alexander Hennessy, the bush pilot, took Hugh Alexander Chapman, his godson, into his Beechcraft on Sioux Lookout airfield, and flew him home, across the smiling wilderness, to Rat Dam and Bearskin and his own folk.

Oh, I'd love to end the story there. But somehow life, over the Height of Land, is not all happy endings.

It is with tears I tell you that before the next winter was out, a measles epidemic crept across that far unpeopled land.

And miraculous little Hugh Alexander Chapman was one of them who died.

The Slosh

Chelsea, our little Welsh corgi, is nine years old now, and has only the one bad habit.

If you allow seven years of our lives for a year of a dog's life, then Chelsea is in her mid-sixties, and ought to have got over some of her earlier prejudices.

But no: as full of vim and muscle as ever, and with her sharp ears forever pointed forward in the position of eternal vigilance characteristic of corgis, she hates cats!

Hates? She has hysterics at the sight or sound of a cat. And since five of our surrounding neighbours are cat fanciers, Chelsea is subject to a lot of hysterics.

Actually, she has never killed a cat. But many a cat has had one or two of its nine lives scared out of it by the rushing golden ball of fury that inhabits our back yard.

Chelsea, of course, is a house-and-garden dog. Except on her summer holidays, when she can range far and loose in a rocky splendour of porcupines, skunks, chipmunks, to all of which she pays polite and distant interest (it is cats she is looking for), she is never on the street except on leash. If we encounter a cat while out walking, it's a fight to hold her.

Over the years, we have tried to inform her that cats have a place in the social structure. We have held family councils. We have most kindly drawn her attention to cats she had not already seen, saying "Nice kitty!" But what happens? Hysterics. Chelsea is of the opinion that cats are a menace to civilization, and she tries her best to convert us.

In the old days, when I shouted at her during one of her hysterics, she merely thought I was joining in the din.

So I devised a little scheme. I keep a quart milk bottle full of water on the table out on the back patio, with a small peanut-butter glass beside it. Whenever Chelsea goes into one of her cat tantrums, I get up and fling a glass of water at her. I always miss; for she is quicker than a squirrel. But the indignity of being sloshed with water seems to penetrate her fevered brain, and she comes and sits on the patio beside me, muttering and moaning her despair.

In the non-patio season, a glass of water carried smartly from the kitchen sink, or upstairs, from the bathroom and flung out a window, does the trick.

But in nine years, it hasn't altered Chelsea's opinion of cats one iota. She is, I am afraid, bigoted.

Last Sunday morning, it was so pleasant that I decided to have my breakfast on the patio amid the last asters of summer. It was around ten o'clock, and very pleasant in the sabbath calm. I shared my toast crusts with Chelsea, and there wasn't a cat or a worry in the world. When I decided to go up to the bathroom to shave, I called Chelsea's attention to the sabbath calm and the golden beauty of the morning, and suggested she be a lady, for once, in consideration of the neighbours who might be sleeping in.

Now, my bathroom has two of those quaint leaded-pane windows, the sills about chin-high to me. There is a radiator under them, which makes it impossible for anybody but a man six and a half feet tall to stick his head out and see into the side entrance, with its little wire gate.

I had hardly laid my razor out before there suddenly exploded, right under my open window in the side entrance, one of Chelsea's hysterics.

Calmly, I filled the plastic mug off the bathroom glass

shelf. Expertly, I tossed the water out the window, uttering, at the same time, the accompanying and traditional snarl of command:

"Gyaarr outa that, ya cat killer!"

(I forgot to mention earlier that I still have my old army voice, after fifty years; a sort of raspy roar.)

Chelsea instantly ceased her racket, and I hoped none of the neighbours had had to turn over in bed. By the slight scuffling sound below, I figured maybe this time I had caught Chelsea fair and square.

However, when I went down after shaving and dressing, she was quite dry. I picked some asters and little 'mums and took them in to the piano; and the peaceful sabbath drifted along.

It was Tuesday that I noticed something odd. Mrs. McCormack across the street was sweeping her front walk. I greeted her cordially, as usual.

She turned her back and went in.

Wednesday, I happened to hear the postman putting our letters through the slot and I got up and opened the door to say hello.

He stepped back and looked at me keenly.

"How are you keeping, Mr. Clark?"

"Fine, fine," I said, picking up the mail. "How's yourself?"

He gave me another long look and walked off.

Thursday, when I got on the bus, Wilkie, one of my around-the-corner neighbours whose yard abuts on mine, came running and climbed aboard behind me.

"Hello, there," I said, heading for a vacant seat.

To my surprise, Wilkie didn't come and join me. He walked past me to another vacant double. I got up and joined him.

"How's things?" I asked.

"Very well, thank you," said Wilkie.

He was quite stiff.

I glanced at him. He was looking out the window.

"I say, old man," I said, "is anything the matter? All right at home? The kids?"

"You know perfectly well what's the matter," said Wilkie.

"How do you mean?" I asked, shocked.

"The way you treated that young couple who just moved into our upper duplex," said Wilkie. "It's all over the neighbourhood."

"I don't know what you're talking about," I said.

"Throwing water on them, and swearing at them," said Wilkie.

"Swearing at them? Water . . . ?" I cried in astonishment.

"They wouldn't even tell me what you called them," accused Wilkie. "They said it was unprintable!"

"When? Where? Whaaa?" I responded.

"As nice a young couple as you ever met," said Wilkie.

"They were in my garden, and they saw you sitting on the patio in yours. And because they had been reading your stuff for years, and it was such a nice, quiet morning, they just thought they would walk around . . ."

"Chelsea!" I exclaimed so explosively that nearly everybody in the bus turned to look at me.

"It was Sunday?" I asked. "In the side entrance?"

"Yes," said Wilkie, flatly.

Excitedly, agitatedly, holding a grip on Wilkie's arm, I explained the whole thing: Chelsea and the milk bottle of water; the bathroom, and how high the windows are; how I fret over what the neighbours think of Chelsea and her hysterics.

"Surely," I said, "surely you have seen me throwing a glass of water at Chelsea!"

"I can't say I have," said Wilkie, still stiff. "But I've often heard you swearing at her, and she stops suddenly."

"SWEARING!" I protested. "All I do is growl! 'Gyaarr outa that, ya cat killer!' "

Everybody in the bus turned and looked reprovingly at me. An elderly lady across the aisle got up and went to a vacant seat up near the driver.

Wilkie's office is two blocks in the opposite direction from mine when we get off the bus. I walked it with him, elaborating, clarifying.

"The poor souls!" I said.

"They thought you were some kind of a nut," said Wilkie, softening.

So we shook hands at the entrance of Wilkie's building.

"Look," he said, "weather permitting, Sunday I will be having the usual barbecue in the garden, after church. You come. I'll invite the neighbours. And you can meet the young couple upstairs."

"Wonderful!" I thanked him. "And I'll bring Chelsea."

"Well, uh . . ." said Wilkie, the cat fancier.

"And demonstrate!" I explained.

Susanna and the Elder

All childhood has some message for us. But after seventy-three years, it is my considered opinion that the age of two, or thereabouts, is the magical age.

Let me demonstrate.

The McKechnie house, whose garden abuts on mine, had stood desolate for weeks. Laurie McKechnie, one of the editors of the Toronto *Telegram*, had died last Christmas and his family had moved away. We neighbours were more than curious as to who would occupy it. Who could make a garden such as Leslie's, the wife of Laurie?

With natural curiosity, faithfully shared by us neighbours, we found it was to be Allan Fleming, art director of one of Canada's biggest advertising agencies, the young man who some years ago designed the unique CN that now adorns the Canadian National Railways' cars all over the continent (and who most indignantly protests the idea that that is all the ideas he ever had).

Even more discreet inquiry revealed that he and his wife had three little children. Ah, well, little children are almost the same as flowers, in a garden.

So here I stood the day the moving vans arrived. I am sure all my neighbours were behind their curtains, watching.

But I was out on my patio, pretending to be taking a small constitutional walk, as becomes the aged.

The first things to come off the moving vans were electrifying. One was a triangular structure, about six feet high, from the crossbar of which hung two swings. The other was what is called a jungle gym, such as you see in playgrounds, also a six-foot structure with crossbars on which children can climb and do cartwheels and hang by their knees like Tarzan.

The moving-van men were obviously the family type. They set down the structures and studied the yard. Then they placed the swing where it would look best; and they brought the jungle gym down toward me and set it up firmly.

"Thank you, gentlemen," I said.

At which moment, there ran from the side drive two children, a girl and a boy. They raced about the big garden, exploring. When they saw me, they slowed down and came toward me cautiously.

"Is that a playhouse?" asked the girl, pointing to the little McKechnie tool shed up against the corner of my fence.

"It WAS a tool shed," I replied. "But NOW it is a playhouse."

"My name," said the girl, stepping forward, "is Elizabeth."

The boy snorted.

"Her name," he said scornfully, "is Martha. And she is seven."

Martha turned away, her face full of bitter realization of the perfidy of brothers.

"Martha," I said, "is a beautiful name. Has nobody told you the story of Martha? She was the sister of Mary."

(It is in St. John, 11:7-42.)

"My name," said the boy, "is Peter. I'm five."

"Good." said I. "My name is Gregory. And I am 105."

They regarded me gravely.

From far up beside the moving vans in the side drive appeared a tiny figure. She came running full belt, feet flung wide, arms held wide, too, in case of the expected tumble. As she toddled and jumped across the unfamiliar lawn, I could see she had a pony tail and her hair was the color of ash leaves in autumn.

"Who," I asked, as she came, "is this?"

"This is Susanna," said Martha. "And she is two years and two months."

Susanna staggered to a halt when she joined us. We stared at each other. Detecting admiration in my gaze, Susanna promptly turned to the jungle gym and started to climb. At each bar, she stopped to see if I was watching. I was. She went up, up, up, with the laborious effort of the two-year-old, until she reached the top.

She held on with one hand and flung the other arm wide. In a clear voice she cried:

> *"I'm king of a cassle*
> *And you're a dirty rassle!"*

With exclamations of dismay, Martha and Peter backed away, and withdrew to explore the tool shed, leaving the stage to Susanna and me.

Now, how do you bridge the gulf between infancy and old age? It is like looking down a long, shadowy corridor.

All I wanted was one nursery rhyme. Just ONE, to counter Susanna. But do you think I could find one? (Ten minutes later, I had a dozen, Hickory-dickory-dock, Little Miss Muffet.)

But there I was, spellbound. And Susanna, triumphant on top of the jungle gym, was watching me. With gestures and every facial expression I could summon I showed her my appreciation.

How, how do you bridge the gulf? Slowly, cautiously, Susanna began to descend the perilous heights. I was going to lose her.

It is like going down a long, grey corridor of time. Perspective is there, but it grows more shadowy. There are filmy curtains of time, like curtains of cobwebs that you have to thrust aside. It is a frightening thing to have to find a nursery rhyme in a crisis.

Susanna reached the ground.

I was back to my Varsity days, down that corridor.

Interesting thumps were coming from the tool shed.

To my delight, Susanna did not leave. She came to the fence and carefully climbed the low stone parapet that foots the wire mesh fence between us. She clung to the fence.

"*Eheu*," I said.

Susanna gave me her profile against the wire mesh, the pony tail shaking.

> *Eheu fugaces, Postume, Postume,*
> *labuntur anni nec pietas moram*
> *Rugis et instanti senectae*
> *Adferet indomitaeque morti.*

It was the best I could do. I was back at least to Varsity.

Susanna was unimpressed. She took up the conversation. I could catch a word here and there, fragments of words, figments of words. But mostly it was just chatter, and a marvellous take-off of a grown-up in conversation. The eyebrows up and down, the eyes from side to side, then lowered, and the pony tail shaking.

When she finished her turn, she gave me her profile again. My turn. I realized she was not a Horatian.

"Don't you know," I asked, "what that means? It goes like this:

> *Alas, how they fly by, Postumus, Postumus,*
> *The years, the swift years. Wrinkles*
> *And old age advancing and . . .*

But I could not say the next word. You do not say that word in front of children.

Susanna took her turn. For thirty seconds, clinging there to the wire fence, she gave me another beautiful representation of a lady in lively gossip, though not a word came through to me.

I was still pushing back down that corridor of memory. The cobwebby curtains . . .

When Susanna gave me her profile, for my turn, I had got back to my high-school days.

Marcellus!

Of course! Marcellus on the misty battlements of Elsinore! I had played Marcellus sixty years ago, as a boy. But then I had played Marcellus many a time thereafter. I can play a scared sentry on the shrouded battlements of Elsinore to the king's taste. For I HAVE been scared, on battlements mistier though less noble than Elsinore's.

I drew myself into attitude of fright. I huskied my voice. Susanna looked at me.

> *Some say that ever 'gainst that season comes*
> *Wherein our Saviour's birth is celebrated*
> *The bird of dawning singeth all night long . . .*

Susanna stared at me. She let go one hand from the wire and flung her arm wide.

"Wheeeeeee!" she cried.

And down she got, carefully, before I could even tell her that the bird of dawning is only a rooster, maybe only an old rooster; and she toddled running off to join Martha and Peter in the tool shed.

So she is a Shakespearean. She does not care for Horace and his ode.

Here I sit, on Christmas Eve, in my den, and *The Tempest* open before me. The winter wind is whistling at my windows and rattling the shutters. My old house is silent, nothing moves.

I am searching *The Tempest* for the passage I want to re-memorize. Is it this one that Abraham Lincoln loved, and millions of others of us unknown?

> *Our revels now are ended. These our actors*
> *As I foretold you were all spirits, and*
> *Are melted into air, into thin air:*
> *And like the baseless fabric of this vision,*
> *The cloud-capped towers*
> *the gorgeous palaces,*
> *The solemn temples, the great globe itself,*

Yea, all which it inherit, shall dissolve;
And like this insubstantial pageant faded,
Leave not a rack behind. We are such stuff
As dreams are made of; and our little life
is rounded with a sleep . . .

No. That's not it. For Susanna, the revels have barely begun. And besides, how could I be Prospero? Prospero was tall and kingly.

Of course, I could make a high pointed paper cap and design stars and crescents on it, in red and blue. That is what distinguishes the magician's cap from the dunce's. And for Prospero's magic cloak, I could use the tartan lap robe from the car. I could draw myself up, up, and maybe look tall and kingly.

Ah, here it is!

Ye elves of hills, brooks, standing
lakes and groves,
And ye that on the sands with printless foot
Do chase the ebbing Neptune, and do fly him
When he comes back; you demi-puppets, that
By moonshine do the green sour ringlets make
Whereof the ewe not bites . . .

Of course! There it is. As I foretold you, all childhood has message for us. By a round-about way, Susanna has got her message to me.

The winter wind is whistling at the windows still, the shutters rattle, the old quiet house is silent.

But at this instant I know that in twelve, fourteen weeks, I can go out to the country and walk the new-bare pastures and find those strange ringlets in the grass, already green. And nobody knows how they come there.

And a week or two after that, I can go to one of the long lake beaches and see the flocks of little sandpipers, the sanderlings, chasing the retreating waves with printless foot and flying back when the wave returns.

That is the message of Susanna.

Spring.

Queen Under the Steps

Wilson, my across-the-street neighbour, overtook me at the local bus stop.

"Have you noticed," he asked, as we sat down in the bus, "that old tomcat around?"

"Can't say I have," I reported.

"It's in my side drive all the time," said Wilson. "The worst-looking old cat you ever saw. It's been around two or three weeks."

"I know most of the cats." I said. "My dog keeps most of them at leg's length."

"I've called the Humane Society twice," said Wilson. "But by the time they arrive, the darn' cat has vanished. My wife – she's very soft about animals – puts out a soup bowl of milk now and then. But it is the WORST old tom-cat . . ."

"The trick," I explained, "is to get your wife to coax it into the house, and THEN phone the Humane Society. It's astonishing the number of stray cats there are in the world . . ."

"We've tried that," said Wilson. "But you can't get near him. We put out milk and try to coax him in. But he just shies off."

"Oh well, what the heck," I said. "A tomcat. He'll probably go away."

"Funny you haven't noticed him," said Wilson. "He's sitting in my side drive half the time."

"Actually," I said, "I don't much notice cats."

So we changed the subject to politics, of which Wilson is very fond.

In the middle of supper, that same evening, Wilson phoned me excitedly.

"Hey!" he said. "That tomcat I was speaking about this morning? It isn't a TOMcat! It's a MAMA cat!"

I swallowed what I was eating.

"The kids heard these funny sounds," said Wilson, "coming from under that trellis thing around our front steps. And sure enough, when I got back from the office, I got a flashlight. And do you know what? She's got a litter of KITTENS under our front steps!"

"O.K., O..K.," I said, anxious to get back to the fish soufflé Mrs. Armstrong, my housekeeper, had prepared. "Phone the Humane Society. Now you've GOT it!"

"Yeah," said Wilson, "I've already phoned them. But the KIDS have seen the kittens. I let them peek through the trellis, and they've SEEN the kittens. A little huddle, a sort of BALL of kittens. And they WANT them!"

"The Humane Society boys will look after that," I said. "Main thing is to look after the old lady."

"The WORST-looking old cat," said Wilson. "All raggedy . . ."

"I'm at supper," I suggested.

"Look," said Wilson, "you know those big pliers you've got? I was wondering if you could come over, as soon as you finish supper, and we'll remove the trellis, so I can get in under the front steps?"

I've got a pair of oversize pliers, with an offset head, that are invincible at pulling nails. And all the neighbors know about them.

So I hurried through my soufflé and even spent less time on the plum preserve than I usually do; and I got the pliers and headed over to Wilson's.

There was already quite a crowd gathered. They were kneeling down, peering through the lattice siding that foots all around Wilson's front steps. There were the three Wilson children, the McDonald twins, age six, young Tony, the professor's son from three doors up, the pretty

little Whiting girl, and half a dozen others I didn't recognize. Cat news appears to spread fast.

Wilson with the flashlight was kneeling among them, letting them peer.

"Good," he said, when I arrived with pliers. "Have a look."

Through the lattice, in the flashlight beam, I saw this frowsy cat, who turned her head proudly aside when the light struck her. Close under her, I could detect the moving, squirming figures of the kittens.

"How many?" I asked Wilson.

"I can't figure," he said. "Maybe three, four?"

"Why don't we wait for the Humane Society boys?" I asked.

There was an immediate uproar of protest from the children.

"I want a kitty! I'm going to have a kitty! You PROMISED me!"

The oldest Wilson, a girl, calmly assured the gathering that she had first choice.

"They're OUR cats," she reminded them.

So Wilson took my pliers and began prying and loosening at the panels of lattice. Being gifted, he pulled a few nails, and off came a panel. It was a pretty low, dark space underneath the steps.

"You're a handier size than I am," said Wilson. "How would you like to crawl under? I'll hold the flash."

When I wriggled down and inched toward the cat, at the farthest corner under the steps, she hissed and spat at me. In the flashlight beam, her mouth was wide and her frightening white teeth were bared high.

I backed up a little.

"Look," I said to Wilson, "I know how to grab dogs. I'm a dog man. But I don't know how to grab a cat . . ."

"Come on," said Wilson.

He had on the old fedora he always puts on after arriving home from the office. I held the flashlight while he scrunched down and wormed his way forward. He took a handful of the dank earth that inhabits under steps and threw it at the old lady. She leaped back and crouched in a farther corner. Wilson picked up the kittens and put them in his hat. And backed out.

We swarmed around.

"Don't touch them," warned Wilson, as the children tried to grab. "Just look."

There were four. Their little eyes were not yet opened, and as they coiled and squirmed in Wilson's hat, their little mouths opened in soundless cries. The old lady came from under the steps and, with tail threshing, walked amidst our legs as the children boiled about.

"Watch her," I cautioned Wilson; for the old lady now and again seemed ready to spring up.

"One for me!" yelled the Wilson girl, jumping up and down.

"And one for us!" cried the McDonald twins. "You PROMISED!"

"Can I have one?" asked the little Whiting girl.

And young Tony, the professor's son, opened his mouth and let go a wild howl.

"The girls," he bawled, "get EVERYTHING!"

And with all the screaming, bawling and hooting and

jumping about, there arrived all of a sudden, with a scrape of tires, a car at the Wilson's side drive.

Out of it leaped a tall, dark man in a ski jacket.

He strode up the drive.

"Good heavens!" he cried.

He knelt down and made curious sounds. The old lady came to him. He picked her up in his arms. And it was like a mother with a baby, the way he rocked and swayed, and patted and stroked the old lady.

He stood up.

"The kittens!" he cried. "Where are the kittens?"

Wilson was showing them to him in his hat. The stranger ran his hand down in amidst them, the way a man might run his hand into a pail of pearls or blueberries.

"The children," said Wilson, "were expecting to have a kitten each."

"HAVE a kitten!" said the stranger, the old lady curved in his embrace. "My dear sir, those kittens are worth hundreds of dollars!"

"Oh, now," I put in.

"This," said the stranger, "is my top queen."

"Queen?" I enquired.

"She sure doesn't look like any queen," said Wilson.

"We call them queens," said the stranger proudly. "They are our breeders. She's been lost three weeks. The cleaning woman left her cage open and she got out. When they are expecting, they often go and hide . . ."

He stroked the old lady and ran his hand in amongst the tiny soundless kittens. There were tears in his eyes.

"Lord knows," he said, "how she got this far. Why, it's twenty, twenty-four blocks! She's got burrs in her fur, the beauty."

"What kind is she?" I, a dog man, asked.

"A Persian," said the stranger grandly, "with a show record unequalled in all America."

She didn't look like my idea of Persians.

"She's been lost," protested the stranger, "three weeks!

Living off heaven knows what. And caring for her kittens! We've haunted the Humane Society. We've travelled miles in the car, hunting. Then a few minutes ago, the Humane Society phoned there was a female with a litter under the steps, the STEPS of this address . . ."

He took the hat from Wilson.

"My wife has put out milk for her?" said Wilson.

"Have you a basket?" asked the stranger.

Wilson went in the side door and down the cellarway. Tony began to howl again. The Wilson girl, the Mc-Donald twins, the lovely little Whiting child, drew apart, in tears, to comfort one another.

When Wilson returned with a bushel basket, ripping up newspaper to make a nest of it, the stranger picked up each kitten from the hat, studied it intently, and placed it in the basket. Then, feet first, he lowered the old lady into it. And they became one ball.

"Children," said the stranger, "these kittens are far too young to be taken from their mother. Besides, they are worth FAR too much for little girls."

"Waugh!" howled Tony. "Girls get everything!"

"Tell you what I'll do," said the stranger reaching into his hip pocket.

He took from his wallet two $10 bills. After studying me and Wilson, he decided Wilson was the householder, and he handed him the money.

"Give each of the little girls $5," he said. "They can get a good little kitten for that. In fact, I'll tell the Humane Society boys to keep their eyes open for four good kittens, and they won't cost ANYTHING. I am so grateful . . ."

He picked up the basket and we all followed down to his car.

"Waaagh," howled Tony, "aw-wauuugh! The girls get everything!"

And, stamping his feet as he ran, he ran for home.

And that is how we nearly got four new cats, four FAMOUS cats, for our neighbourhood.

What Mrs. Allery Saw

Right after supper, it was McDodd at my front door.

He looked excited and embarrassed.

"Sorry to bother you," he said.

"Come in, man," I said.

McDodd lives in the next block south. His back yard touches a corner of mine; but I am not very well acquainted with him, because of the jungle of lilac bushes and sweet syringa at the foot of his garden.

"Have you," asked McDodd, sitting down, "been stuck with one of these phony $20 bills yet?"

"No, SIR!" I assured him.

"Well, I was," said McDodd. "Three weeks ago. I don't know how I got it. Can't figure who passed it on to me. But when I took some money to my bank, they spotted this phony. And there I was!"

"Out $20," I figured.

"They not only wouldn't accept it," he said, "but they told me if I happened to be caught with it in my possession, I could be charged with possessing and presumably PASSING counterfeit money."

"You were in a spot," I agreed.

"So they told me to take it straight to the police," said McDodd, "and try to remember where I had got it. I took it to the cops. But darned if I could figure where I had got it. I imagine somebody gave it to me in all innocence. But it is a funny feeling to hand $20 to the police."

"No change," I sympathized.

McDodd glanced about the room in obviously growing confusion.

"Clark₁₆," he said, "you're a newspaperman. You are more acquainted with the police than most of us . . ."

"You mean about that twenty bucks?" I interjected.

"No, no!" said McDodd. "My mother-in-law."

"Mrs. Allery?" I protested.

"My RESIDENT mother-in-law!" said McDodd, with a touch of bitterness. "I've got to be frank with you, Clark. She's a peeper."

"A . . . uh?" I checked.

"You know how old people get," explained McDodd. "They go kind of funny. Shoplifters, and that sort of thing. Well, my mother-in-law is a peeper."

I was amazed. I see Mrs. Allery, really, only once a year, when the lilacs are in bloom. If she sees me in my garden, she calls to me; and pushing her way through the jungle of lilac bushes and sweet syringa, in the month of June, she presents me with a gorgeous bouquet of lilac: mauve, Persian, purple, white. And over the fence, we have a great annual conversation, and she tells me all the gossip of the neighbourhood in which I live.

"Peeper!" I objected.

For it is true the rest of the year, old Mrs. Allery waves to me from upstairs windows, yoo-hoo. And I wave cordially.

"She knows EVERYTHING," said McDodd, "that goes on, including what days you have breakfast in bed. And what you have."

"Oh, NOW!" I demurred.

"Here's the point," said McDodd. "There is a window in the back room of our third floor, the attic. It isn't really a room, it's a sort of store room. There is a small window, high up. You can't see out of it, unless you stand on a five-foot stepladder. A chair won't do."

McDodd took a deep breath.

"Well, sir, my old mother-in-law even peeps out THAT window. As you know, our next-door neighbour has a rooming house – one of those big old houses. And this window of ours looks right down into a room on the second floor next door."

"Go on," I urged, for McDodd was weakening.

"After I lost that phony $20 bill," he said, "I naturally talked about it around the house."

"Naturally," I encouraged.

"My mother-in-law, a couple of nights ago, informed me that the man who occupies that room you can see into from our store-room window," said McDodd, lowering his voice, "is ENGRAVING!"

I held my breath.

"When I turned in that counterfeit bill," he continued, "one of the cops mentioned that he had a hunch that these phonies were being produced right in THIS NEIGHBORHOOD! So I went up to the attic and had a look."

"What does he look like?" I asked.

"Middle-aged," said McDodd. "You can only see the top half of him as he sits at a table under his window. He has a strong desk lamp. There he sits in his shirt sleeves, WORK-ING at something. Occasionally, you can see something in his hand, when he raises it. And it looks like a needle or a tiny knife. Every few minutes, he puts one of those black magnifiers the watchmakers stick in their eye ..."

"That's called a loupe," I told him.

"And he stares at what he is working on. Now, hear this! The cops told me the BIG trouble about these phony $20 bills is that the crooks keep changing the serial numbers, so they can't put out a warning, or identification."

We stared at each other.

"You've seen a lot of funny things in your life, as a reporter," said McDodd. "That's why I have come to you, to see if you would mind coming around to my place and have a look and see if we should call the police."

"Maybe," I said, "he's just a stamp collector. Does he look like a stamp collector?"

"What do they look like?" asked McDodd.

"Oh, sort of middle-aged and kind of concentrated," I

explained, "if you know what I mean. Maybe this fellow is a stamp collector."

"With NEEDLES in his hand?" demanded McDodd. "And other little shiny tools?"

I got up.

"I'll come," I said. "Wait till I change out of my slippers."

In five minutes we were at the McDodds', one block south. Old Mrs. Allery was waiting for us.

"Follow me," she directed.

We climbed to the third floor, and Mrs. Allery opened the door to the store room.

"Sssshhh!" she warned.

We groped our way through the trunks and cartons with which the store room was crowded. I could see a five-foot stepladder at the high window. Mrs. Allery, a nimble old lady, climbed up first and cautiously raised her head over the window sill.

"He's AT it," she hissed, coming down.

I got up on the ladder and peeped. He was a middle-aged man, in his shirt sleeves, going bald. The table at which he was working was under the window, so that I could see only his torso. He was working swiftly with his hands, no doubt about it. While I watched, he put the loupe in his eye and bent over, studying his work. When he raised his hand, to take the loupe out of his eye, I saw a small glittering object in it.

I got down.

"Where's the phone?" I asked.

I called the district police station. I got my friend, Detective McEwan. Calmly, without excitement, I explained the situation. Described the room, the man with the small bright tools, the loupe in his eye . . .

"I'll be right over," said Detective McEwan.

In less than five minutes, he arrived, his mate sitting outside in the plain, family car.

Mrs. Allery led us up.

And Detective McEwan cautiously climbed the ladder. He watched for five full minutes.

When McEwan got down, we went downstairs.

"Well," he said, "there is something peculiar going on there. I can't figure it out. But I haven't got a warrant. I can't go barging in . . ."

You can't be a newspaper reporter for fifty or one hundred years without becoming quick-witted.

"Hold it!" I commanded.

Even Mrs. Allery was quiet.

"What's the name of the people who run this rooming house?" I asked.

"Miss McAdam," said Mrs. Allery, "a fine, charming . . ."

"How long has she had it?" was my next shrewd question.

"Four years," said McDodd.

"Five," said Mrs. Allery.

"o.k.," I plotted, in the fashion well known to all old reporters. "We'll leave our hats here. We'll CALL on Miss McAdam. I will, laughingly, tell her that, as a child, I LIVED in this house. And we, just a gathering of old friends, were talking about childhood memories."

"Aha," said Detective McEwan.

"And," I said, "I remembered hiding four silver dollars under a loose board in that built-in bookcase we can see from your window, on the far wall . . ."

"You should be working for us," said Detective McEwan, giving me a pat on the shoulder.

"So," I concluded, "I had forgotten all about those boyhood memories. And we were just WONDERING if, after all these years . . ."

We left our hats at McDodd's. Detective McEwan signalled his partner to leave the car and go around to the back of the house. Miss McAdam answered the door when we rang. With laughter and apologetic airs and like a bunch of sentimentalists, we explained our mission. I wanted to see if there were the four silver dollars . . .

"Is there still," I asked, "a built-in bookcase along the left-hand wall of the room at the back of the second floor? That was my room." (I had seen it not fifteen minutes before.)

"There is!" exclaimed Miss McAdam delighted. "It's still there!"

"Is there . . . ?" I asked.

"Fortunately," said Miss McAdam, "Mr. Crawford, who has that room, is in."

"Oh, we don't want to disturb . . ." I protested.

"He won't mind in the least," assured Miss McAdam. "As nice a gentleman as you ever met. He's been with me three months and . . ."

McDodd, Detective McEwan and I exchanged significant glances. It was three months that the phony twenties have been loose in the neighborhood.

"Yes," said Miss McAdam, leading us off up the stairs. "He often has gentlemen come to see him."

I had a little trouble getting Mrs. Allery behind me. I wanted Detective McEwan next. He had a little trouble getting her behind him, as we mounted the stairs. She came next; McDodd last.

"Mr. Crawford?" called Miss McAdam, rapping lightly on the door.

"Yes."

"Could we see you a minute?"

"Certainly."

The key turned in the lock. The door was flung wide. Mr. Crawford was just taking the loupe out of his eye.

At the very first glance, I recognized the layout. Under the window through which we had been peeping was a long narrow table. Clamped to it, slim and silvery, was a jeweller's pin-vise. In the pin-vise, was a fish hook, size 6, already dressed with some feathers. All over the table were strewn plastic envelopes containing feathers of every precious description.

"MISTER Crawford!" I cried. "You are a fly-tier!"

"That I am," he said heartily. "Come in, folks."

I led. I bent over the little vise. Even though only half done, I could see it was perfect. It was to be a John Sutton's red badger.

"The badger hackles," I said, "tented."

"And, of course," said Mr. Crawford, "doubled."

I picked up envelope after envelope and admired the hackles, badger, honeydun, Andalusian blue.

"Are you a commercial fly-tier?" I asked in admiration.

"Gosh, no," said Mr. Crawford, "I'm an accountant in a firm of lawyers. I just tie them for myself and a few friends."

Mrs. Allery, after a few sniffs, had left the room and I could hear her heels stamping down the stairs. Miss McAdam followed her, for a little gossip. Nobody remembered about the fictitious four silver dollars. McDodd quietly tiptoed out. Detective McEwan stood for a minute or two, while Mr. Crawford got out a cardboard box to show me a collection of the flies he had tied over the winter. Then he went to the casement window at the back of the room – not the one we had been peeping in – and called down:

"O.K., George! Meet me in the car."

Mr. Crawford observed this with some surprise.

When Detective McEwan smiled at us and departed, Mr. Crawford followed to the stairway and watched him go.

"Now," said Mr. Crawford, "what business would HE be in?"

"He's a detective," I explained.

Which all goes to show you how we trout fishermen happen to get together, one way and another.

The Night
George Called

It was 11:10 P.M. when the phone rang. I was asleep.

"Hi!" said the easy voice. "This is George."

"George!" I exclaimed, waking up. "How in the world are you?"

George Miller is one of my summer friends. The Miller cottage is third west of ours at the beach. I don't see him from the end of August to the beginning of the next July. And don't often think of him in between.

"And how's Elsie?" I inquired cordially, though I was standing there in only my pyjama tops.

"Fine, the last time I saw her," said George. "At Christmas."

My head began to swim. George and Elsie Miller are, to my mind, two of the most attached people on earth. In the summer, it is a pleasure, and maybe a little amusing, to see them walking along the beach hand in hand, after thirty years of marriage.

"George," I said carefully, "how are things going? What's up?"

"The reason I called," he replied, "is I've just had a message from Dad. He's coming down to see me tomorrow. And I was wondering if you could drop over around 8. He'd love to see you."

I pinched the handiest part of me with my free hand to see if I were awake. You don't pinch yourself when you are dreaming.

For George's dad has been dead 12 years. Dear old Mr. Miller. I attended his funeral.

"He's coming down?" I husked.

"Yes," said George. "He got a message through to me not ten minutes ago. And he specially asked to see you."

"How . . . uh . . .?" I began. But couldn't think of how to ask it.

"So try to make it, will you?" urged George.

At that instant, I detected a strained quality in George's voice. It was more excited. I know his voice well, since we spend a great deal of our summers together exploring the woods back of the beach. He is a brilliant amateur naturalist. And he talks, normally, in a calm, reflective tone. But now there was a definite stress in it.

"Sure I'll come," I said as cheerily as I could. I did not want to break off. Elsie? What about Elsie? How is it I had heard nothing about THAT from any of our mutual acquaintances?

"George," I asked casually, "who's looking after you?"

"Looking AFTER me?" he said, with an instant note of suspicion in his voice. "Marian, of course. Who else?"

Marian. My mind raced around trying to recollect any Marian. I rubbed my eyes and tried to shake the sleep out of my bewildered head.

Marian! Why, there was a little bit of a girl named Marian who worked as a filing clerk in George's office. She could be no more than eighteen or nineteen. She was a guest for a week last summer at the Miller's.

"o.k., George," I said hoarsely. "Tomorrow, eh? Eight p.m."

And we hung up.

I did not go right back to bed. I sat down on the cold little chair beside the telephone table.

You read about things like this in novels. You see situations like this on TV dramas. But you never expect to meet them in real life.

Decent old George! Poor happy Elsie! Things like this must come out of the blue like evil great birds. Probably George had suffered a breakdown. Maybe he had just quietly gone off his head. Possibly he had got into one of those stages of desperation that middle-aged men are said to experience.

He must, of course, be right off his head. A message from his father, dead twelve years. I sat and remembered old Mr. Miller. We were both collectors of old books. In our travels about the country, we searched second-hand book stores. He kept his eye open for any early Canadiana about fishing or hunting or natural history, like botany or birds. And I kept my eye peeled for anything about the history of the Church of England in Canada, which was old Mr. Miller's chief interest. We would exchange our finds by mail, even-stephen. And in summer, when he was at the cottage, we would spend the evenings discussing books.

Sitting there on the cold telephone chair, I thought, for a moment, of what books I might take with me tomorrow night, when I went over to George's.

Shaking free of such thoughts, I figured what practical steps I should take. The only man I knew at George's office was Fleming, a fellow executive in the insurance business they ran. It was too late at night to disturb Fleming, and anyway I didn't know his initials, or where he lived.

Should I call any of the neighbours up at the beach? Surely some of them must have heard the news? But now it was 11:30 P.M.

I went back to bed and tossed and turned, thinking of the sad things that happen to the nicest people.

At 7 I woke. My mind was on George instantly. I sat long enough to make sure I hadn't dreamed of that tragic telephone call.

At 9 sharp I called Fleming at their office.

"Look, old chap," I said, "I want to speak to you confidentially about George. He isn't right near, is he?"

"No," said Fleming.

"Well, don't mention my name," I cautioned. "But tell me: How IS George?"

"Fine, fine," said Fleming. "Why?"

"Well, something has happened," I said, "that has caused me to worry about his health . . ."

"As a matter of fact," said Fleming, lowering his voice, "now that you ask, he has been going to a doctor periodically for the past two or three months. I understand it is something about his gall bladder, and he had to take tests."

"Mmm-hmmm," I said. "Otherwise, he seems in good shape? Doesn't act a little oddly?"

"Oh, no," laughed Fleming. "No more than usual. George has always been a bit of a character, you know."

"Mmm-hm," I said. "By the way, we see a lot of each other up at the cottage. Last summer, they had a little girl from the office up for a week. Name of Marian."

"Oh, yes, Marian," said Fleming. "She left us last Christmas."

Christmas!

Elsie!

I thanked Fleming, after ensuring that he would not let on to George that I had called. Now, what? I could call some of their neighbours from up at the beach. Surely they would have tipped me off, if they had known about Elsie. And Marian. But after long reflection, I figured that in cases of this kind, the human, the humane thing to do, is not to spread the scandal.

At noon, on my way to lunch, I dropped in at my doctor's office, which is fairly downtown. He and I fish together. Our relation is not entirely professional. I recounted the whole affair to him, in detail.

"Greg," he said, "you go. Take some old books with you. Face the thing. And if, in your opinion, the poor chap is deranged, then you get in touch tomorrow with – what's his name?"

"Fleming," I said.

"And get your friend into the doctor's hands."

"Right," said I.

"Especially if that kid – what's her name?"

"Marian."

"Is there," said the doctor.

On my way home, at 5 P.M., I dropped in to my favourite antique book store. I could find nothing about the history of the Church of England in Canada, but I got three tattered old books about Methodist missionaries in the North.

I am an Old Soldier. But it was with trepidation that I rang the bell of the Miller apartment at 8 P.M.

I went up the elevator.

Elsie opened the door.

"Elsie!" I cried.

"Greg!" said she, stepping back with every expression of delight.

"Hell-O!" called George from inside, coming out, book in hand, as usual. "To what are we indebted for the honour of this visit?"

They led me into the living room.

George looked his old self. I could see no sign of any Marian, could hear no sounds.

"Well, well, well," he said. "I didn't look forward to seeing you until July. But I've got here . . ."

And he showed me a new publication from the United States about the buttercup family, which is one of our biggest headaches up at the beach. (But we found, last year, the virgin's bower, *Clematis virginiana,* which was a hell of a surprise to us.) When George leaned over me, showing me the book, I was a little tense.

"What are these?" he asked, picking up the three old books I had brought.

"Oh," I said, "they're not anything to do with the history of the Church of England in Canada. They're Methodist. But I thought . . ."

"Ah," cried George to Elsie, "he remembers dear old Dad!"

I let the conversation wander around.

"When you phoned me last night." I began.

"Last NIGHT?" said George.

"Didn't you phone me last night?"

"No, I didn't."

"Well, I was SURE it was you," I said. "We had quite a conversation."

"What time?" asked George.

"It was about 11:10," I said, "or maybe a little after."

"It sure wasn't me," said George, sitting on the arm of Elsie's chair. "We were at the theatre until close to 11. And then we showed off by going to one of those nighteries for supper. We didn't get home until when?"

"Nearly 1," said Elsie, proudly.

So I never mentioned the matter. We had a lovely evening over the botanical books, and are looking forward, this summer, to identifying three or maybe four of the buttercup family that have eluded us. But I could not keep my mind off that other George, who had called the wrong number, and who, right now, would be waiting for his Dad's old friend to turn up.

However, it all goes to show you how dangerous a thing it is to fear the worst.

The Riot

It only goes to show you how small a thing it takes to create a riot.

Tom Biggs lives in that little buff-coloured brick house across the street there, with the window boxes. Fifth house along.

Tom is an elderly widower, like myself. A by-the-day woman comes in Mondays, Wednesdays and Fridays to do the dishes, make the bed, do the laundry. And each weekend, either Saturday or Sunday, Lucille, Tom's daughter, arrives for the day with her three children, a boy of nine, a girl, seven, and a small boy, four

Tom gets in a supply of minced round steak, or wieners and buns, and prepares lunch for them while Lucille goes over the house tidying up whatever the by-the-day woman has neglected.

Around two o'clock, after lunch, Tom comes across to pay me a little visit; and we go and sit on my back patio.

"Greg," he says, heavily, "I LOVE my grandchildren. But I'm good for only about two hours. Three at the most."

"It's their energy," I explain.

"Energy?" protests Tom. "They're wild! They race all over the house, yell all over the garden, fight over the TV . . ."

"It only lasts a few years, Tom," I soothe. "Pretty soon they'll be teenagers; and then you will hardly ever see them."

"I feel guilty," says Tom, "sneaking over here. To get

away from them! It doesn't seem natural. But after about two hours, I get impatient. I can FEEL my blood pressure going up."

"It's natural, Tom," I assure him. "When we were young, raising our children, Nature gave us a built-in patience and understanding. But when we grow old, as we lose the power of generation, we lose the things that went with it, like tireless patience and forbearance."

"Aw, I feel like a fraud," says Tom. "When they arrive, I am all exuberance and delight. I REALLY feel it. I hug them and even join in their fun, whatever it is. But by the time I am in the kitchen getting the hamburgers ready, and they come in and start horsing around, I begin to feel a little tired. And when Lucille is doing the dishes, and the kids are fighting over which TV program to get, and pulling the knobs off, I am ready to explode."

"Why don't you?" I ask.

"Lucille would never forgive me," says Tom. "So that's why I come over here. I hope you don't mind."

He knows I don't.

Now, before we come to the riot, I must tell you that four or five years ago, at the height of the cigarette scare, Tom gave up smoking and took to eating candy instead. Then two years ago, he gave up his before-dinner drink of Scotch. And ate more candy.

He buys candy bars for the grandchildren.

But for himself, considering his sacrifices, he buys a favourite two-pound box of miniature chocolates. This he hides behind the books in the top shelf of his bookcase. Whenever I drop in on him, he pulls the books aside and offers me a chocolate. I decline, because I have a pipe in my teeth. He takes two or three chocolates and puts the box back in hiding.

Last Saturday was the riot.

Just about 2 P.M.

The following particulars I have gathered in their proper order after interviewing all concerned – Tom, Lucille, the children, the Williamson boy who rang the fire alarm . . .

Lunch was over. Lucille had finished the dishes, and was upstairs in the front bedroom with the youngest boy, the four-year-old.

The two older children were out in the garden climbing on the fence to watch Mrs. Abernethy, who lives in that next house beyond Tom's, lighting a small bonfire to burn up garden trash.

Tom came through the kitchen, where he had been tidying up after Lucille (the way old men do, who like fiddling in kitchens).

And THERE, fair in the middle of the green broadloom rug of the living room, was one of his chocolates!

Tom, as I have explained, was already close to the boiling point. In fact, he was about to walk across to my place.

He halted and glared at the chocolate. It was obviously a chocolate brazil nut, one of his favourites, a crisp little nut encased in rich chocolate.

The children had found his hidden treasure!

Blood pressure mounting, as he recalled that not half an hour before he had given each of them a big fat candy bar, Tom's sense of grievance came to the peak.

He strode over and picked up the chocolate.

But it wasn't a chocolate.

It was a June bug.

When Tom felt its scratchy legs and stared at it for a wild instant, he flung it from him, at the same time uttering a loud yell:

"YEEEEE-OOOOWWW!"

At this moment, Mrs. Abernethy's little bonfire had taken good hold, and a cloud of smoke billowed up. A good whiff of it entered the side windows of Tom's house.

Lucille, a young woman of great presence of mind, hearing the wild yell from below and smelling the smoke

pouring in, grabbed her youngest child and headed for the open window.

Screaming "Fire! Fire!" she shoved the little boy out the window on to the veranda roof, and got one leg of her own across the window sill.

It was at this time, attracted either by Tom's yell or by Lucille's screams, that I reached my upstairs window.

A stranger passing by was racing across to climb Tom's veranda railing to take the little boy from his mother's grasp; or else to get a closer look at Lucille's leg, remarkably exposed as she straddled the window sill, struggling to get out.

And already young Williamson, aged seventeen, a fine young chap who lives on my side of the street opposite Tom's, had gone by me on tremendous strides to smash the glass in the fire-alarm box on the telephone post at the corner, and pull the alarm.

Young Williamson's dog, Buster, a collie, had gone with him. And as they passed the Johnstons', to the west of me two doors, the Johnstons' Labrador, Gunner, aroused by all the screaming and running, came tearing out the side drive and joined the chase. Buster thought he was being attacked, and the dog fight began, right in the middle of the street.

By which time, the fire sirens, coming from only six blocks west of us, were rising, closer, closer.

Naturally, I was immobilized by astonishment at all these activities and was about to leave my window and hurry out to the aid of Tom, when Tom himself, in his shirt sleeves, appeared on the veranda, looking very surprised.

All the neighbours were out on their verandas and some were hurrying toward Tom's.

The hose reel being first to arrive, had to roar to a furious halt, its siren moaning low, because of the dog fight in the middle of the pavement, with young Williamson trying to separate them. The hook and ladder came next and drew up behind the hose reel. Then the fire captain arrived in his red car.

I decided to come downstairs and investigate.

One of the firemen of the hose reel, in his long rubber boots, waded in and kicked the dogs apart. The fire captain left his car and advanced for the reckoning.

Young Williamson frankly confessed he had pulled the fire alarm box on hearing Lucille screaming "Fire!"

Lucille frankly confessed she had indeed screamed from the upstairs window on hearing a wild shout from downstairs and smelling smoke.

Mrs. Abernethy, in her gardening gloves and apron, frankly confessed to lighting a small bonfire to burn garden rubbish, in defiance of the city by-law against air pollution.

The fire captain was taking notes of names and particulars in the midst of all us kindly neighbours gathered around, a circle augmented moment by moment by strangers, since traffic had come to a halt.

"Sir," said young Williamson, whom we all like, "ever since I was a little boy I have dreamed of ringing that fire alarm. I'm sorry."

The fire captain gave him a particularly friendly smile.

"I understand," he said.

At this moment, Lucille's little girl, the seven-year-old, who was limping, piped up:

"Granddad," she said, "I never knew you could yell so LOUD! I fell off the fence!"

"Ah, yes," said the fire captain. "What was that wild shout you heard from downstairs?"

Lucille turned to Tom.

"Well," he said, abashed, "I picked up what I thought was a chocolate, and it was a June bug."

"You didn't EAT it?" exclaimed the fire captain.

"Good heavens, no!" said Tom, above the sounds of amusement from the assembly. "I was a little over-wrought at the moment, and when I felt its scratchy legs, I just flung it . . . and yelled!"

So the party broke up. The dogs were making friends again, with that Labrador and collie air of realizing that it was all a misunderstanding. The fire reels drove away, their quiet bells signalling the all-clear. Traffic resumed. I shook hands with young Williamson. The stranger who had rushed across to help Lucille off the veranda roof shook hands with her a little self-consciously.

Being something of an amateur entomologist, I went back with Tom and Lucille to get the June bug out of the house. I found it walking along the top of a picture frame and took it out and threw it free.

"You didn't squash it?" protested Tom.

"As an actor in this drama," I said, "it deserves its freedom."

"Daddy," asked Lucille, "you said you were overwrought. What do you mean?"

"Darling," said Tom, giving me a sly look, "I don't know. Maybe I had over-cooked the hamburgers or something."

And he gave her a hug.

"Judy," said Lucille, "turned her ankle when she fell off the fence. I've got runs in BOTH my stockings. I think we've had enough excitement for today. Would you mind if I took the children home?"

"My dear," said Tom, "I understand."

So when they left, Tom came over and we sat on my back patio reflecting on all the riot a little thing like a June bug can incite.

Provided, of course, that all the human ingredients of a riot are primed and ready for ignition.

Miss L. Bruce
A Love Story

I never even knew her first name.

Yet for three years of my life, she dominated every day, every hour. I was putty in her hands.

She was a tall, dark, spare woman. I imagine she was in her mid-thirties when I first met her. She had firm cheek bones, the skin tight over them. Her eyes, not large, behind shining steel-rimmed spectacles, were intensely dark, and always simmering or smouldering with either anger or humour. It took us several weeks to be sure that it was humour.

Carrying her pointer, as big, in our eyes, as a billiard cue, she would walk slowly up and down the aisles as we bent to our desks. We were not afraid of her. Her skirts, usually maroon, swept the schoolroom floor.

We had her for three years, Junior Third, Senior Third, Junior Fourth. These are now generally called Grades 5, 6 and 7. In the country schools in those days, it was not uncommon to have the same teacher for four or five years. But in city schools it was most unusual to have the same teacher from one grade to the next. We had Miss Bruce three years. She was promoted with us.

I was never higher than No. 26 in a class of thirty-four. Arithmetic was my ruin. I just COULDN'T get it through my head. To this day, when I have to add up a column of figures, my left hand creeps out of sight, under the desk, to carry. Carry three. Carry five.

And fractions. Or percentages! Let us say it is the arithmetic period. The problem before us is as follows:

Farmer Jones took twenty dozen eggs to market. He sold twelve dozen at fifteen cents a dozen. He sold six dozen at twelve cents a dozen. He sold the remainder at ten cents. What was the average price Farmer Jones received for his eggs?

We bent to our exercise books. All would be silence, except for sniffling and scraping.

"Gregory?" Miss Bruce would say.

Now, all this problem had done for me so far was to conjure up the picture of Farmer Jones's farm. It would be early morning. Over the fields the mist would be lying. The roosters crowing. The cows mooing at the gate. The horses stamping in the stable. And out the farmhouse door would be coming Farmer Jones and a boy about my age, ten, with baskets on his arms to collect twenty dozen eggs.

As I scrambled to my feet the classroom would erupt with snorts and snickers. Everybody knew I was the dunce in arithmetic. With a wave of her dark slim hand, Miss Bruce would quell the snickers.

"Tell us, Gregory," she would say, "what signs and wonders you beheld on your way to school today."

So I would tell them, for instance, that at the mansion of Mrs. Timothy Eaton, at the corner of Lowther avenue and Spadina, the gardeners were putting in the spring annuals.

"How many gardeners?"

"Three."

"What flowers were they planting?"

"Geraniums ... uh ..."

"On your way home, Gregory," Miss Bruce would say, "stop and see what other plants they are putting in. You may sit down."

She was not making fun of me. For in the next breath, she might ask, perhaps, whichever of my seatmates had snorted loudest; or even one of the clever, bland-faced No. 1 girls up at the front of the class, to stand and report what

THEY had seen on their way to school. Stage-struck, they would stand embarrassed. Apparently they had seen nothing on their way to school. Whereupon, it being arithmetic period after all, she would ask one of the tongue-tied clever ones to read the solution of Farmer Jones's problem.

What she was doing, of course, was getting me into the act. I was only one of the backward pupils at the rear of the classroom. She got us all into the act, according to our bents. The next worst arithmetic boy to me could read swiftly, accurately and with style. Miss Bruce would ask him to read to us. Stanley, a boy two or three years older than the rest of us at the back of the class (he wore long pants, that's how OLD he was!) was a hero in the whole school because he was the champion pitcher of one of the sandlot baseball teams that flourished in every few city blocks. One day Stanley put up his hand eagerly in response to one of Miss Bruce's questions. To his horror, Miss Bruce selected him from the forest of hands. Big Stanley rose and stood confused and blushing. He didn't know the answer. He sat down.

In a few minutes, Miss Bruce called on Stanley to stand up.

"Stanley, I believe you have a baseball in your desk?"

"Yes."

"Would you take it, please, and from where you are, show us how you hit the doorknob."

And Miss Bruce pointed to the doorknob up at the far corner of the classroom. Stanley eagerly took the ball, wound up dramatically and hit the doorknob square on the nose. The whole class, even the clever-faced No. 1 girls up front, scrambled to retrieve the ball clattering around our feet, and hand it to Miss Bruce.

As she gave the ball back to Stanley, she said:

"You have something called perfect co-ordination, Stanley. It is something to be proud of."

Before we were half way through Junior Third, or Grade 5, we all knew Miss Bruce was far more interested in us backward ones at the back of the class than in her bright pupils. Often, she would bring her chair down from the little platform on which her desk stood and sit with us.

They have more interesting titles for us nowadays; but we backward children were mostly kept in until four o'clock, three days out of five, for special coaching. But it was fun. For the next stupidest arithmetician to me would be asked to read from the Third Reader; Stanley would be asked to show how to hold the ball, with the fingers just so; and I would be told to tell how the roofers put the tar and gravel on a roof – a procedure I had just witnessed that noon. And the small dark shy girl who stammered so badly would be asked to go to the blackboard and copy out a sentence Miss Bruce had written above. That little girl, age nine, I suppose, could write with the flowing ease of Miss Bruce herself.

"That is beautiful!" Miss Bruce would say, as the girl resumed her seat among us. (There were more fights in the school yard and on the way home over that little chubby girl than over any other cause. Let anyone, boy or girl, mock her, and it was a bloody nose. In Grade 5, in those days, you could sock a girl for cause.)

When the summer came and we felt we were all parting company to move to the next grade, Miss Bruce held a little court. She had a small speech for each of us. For me it was:

"Gregory, don't be afraid! There is more to life than arithmetic."

And she lent me Chester A. Reed's *Bird Guide*, a small brown pocket book illustrating in colour all the birds of this country.

"You can bring it back," she said, "in September. You like seeing things, Gregory. See if you might like to know the wild birds."

This was the instant birth of the love of nature that has been the joy of my life for the sixty-five years since.

On my return to enter Senior Third, Grade 6, imagine my feelings on finding Miss Bruce sitting smiling at the desk in the room to which our class was directed. She was promoted too. Soon the fog deepened for me. I met grammar. And grammar was more incomprehensible to me than arithmetic. With simple, lovely things like words, how can you fit them into pickle jars of laws? It became, in my 10th year, a question whether I should spend my time, kept in each day, on arithmetic or grammar. But still Miss Bruce brought her chair down to the back of the class, and still Big Stanley and the rest of us showed off our non-academic talents, and when summer came again, Miss Bruce lent me, at our farewell party in the classroom, Rudyard Kipling's *Just So Stories*, recently published.

"You will learn more grammar from this," she said, "than from anything I can teach you. You can bring it back to me in September."

Yes, we had her for the third year, in which year she lent me Kipling's *Kim* and took me to show me how to join the Public Library which was away downtown. And all our gang, clever and backward, stayed together until we were at last promoted into Senior Fourth, or Grade 8, the fatal Entrance Year.

Sam Richardson, assistant principal, was our new teacher.

"I understand Gregory," he said to me in front of all, "you have the gift of the gab. I am afraid that will not help you with me. I see by your report that you are very poor in arithmetic and grammar. So we will spend the coming year on those two subjects, principally. Understand?"

I understood.

That was a bare, toilsome, forgotten year out of my life. All I remember of it were the schemes and stratagems I devised for dropping into Miss Bruce's classroom at recess and after hours. And I even braved the dangers inherent in teacher's pet by walking with her after school down to the street-car line on her way home. And being allowed to carry her satchel of books and papers. We talked of India and the wide world.

"I dream," she said, "of saving money enough to visit India some day."

Well, we passed our entrance, under the strong hand of Sam Richardson, every one of us, including Stanley. And I entered the fabled world of high school, where there was Latin and Greek, both with grammars a backward child could understand, not a hodge-podge Chinese puzzle like English grammar. And a debating society, and a literary society, and a school LIBRARY, quiet and stately, where you could visit after four until the caretaker threw you out at five thirty. The ogres of algebra and geometry I met and conquered with the aid of special coaching. And when I got my matriculation, I wrote my first love letter to Miss Bruce.

It was a letter in which I told her I now knew what she had been teaching us in those three years now long behind me. She was teaching us courage.

She was telling us we were good for SOMETHING. Even the gift of the gab. I never posted that letter. It sounded mushy to me. And sixty years ago, to be mushy was the same as being square today. My second love letter I never posted to her was written when I was thrown out of the university for failing my first year twice due to the time I spent hanging around the office of the undergraduate newspaper, *The Varsity*; and endless hours in the great university library, when I should have been at lectures.

In that letter, I told her I knew where I was going now, and that was to be a newspaper reporter, and I thanked her for the three years in which she had excited me to look, look, look at the beautiful, strange world. I didn't post it, because it sounded a little high-falutin' for a cub re-porter.

My last unposted letter to Miss Bruce was written in a dugout north of Arras, France. In that war, we always car-ried an unposted letter to our mother and father, and one to our wife or sweetheart. These were to be found in our paybook if we were killed, to say goodbye. My third letter was to Miss Bruce, thanking her for telling me something I thought of as I led my platoon in the winter night up the line for a tour of eighteen days' duty.

I imagined I saw the tall, serene, maroon figure of Miss Bruce.

"Gregory, don't be afraid," I thought she said. "There is more to life than death."

Well, I wasn't killed. And when the ship that brought me home came into Halifax harbour, I stood in the stern and one by one tore up the three farewell letters and threw them into the wind.

Now, how do you explain that never in all these years did I walk the few blocks to the old school to see Miss Bruce? You explain it. I cannot. Is it shyness? Is it fear of losing something precious, tying you to childhood?

In the early 1930s I got on the Bloor street car.

There, ten feet from me sat Miss Bruce. She was much older than I held her in memory. But she was as straight as ever. On her head a little maroon hat. Her black-gloved hands folded in her lap. It was, as you can believe, the moment of truth for me. I had only to go to Christie street, a few blocks. I had little time. Less time than a man with a sword.

I got up and walked from strap to strap until I stood before her. I reached down and took one of her black-gloved hands.

"Miss Bruce?" I said.

She raised her eyes, dark and shimmering still, behind the steel-rimmed spectacles.

"Yes?"

"I'm Gregory," I said.

"Yes?"

"Gregory Clark," I said. "You had me in Junior Third, Senior Third, Junior Fourth, remember?"

Miss Bruce studied me with an intense expression.

"You lent me *Kim*," I said. "And *Just So Stories*."

"Yes?" she said.

"You remember," I said, "about not being afraid? Not being afraid of arithmetic? Or grammar?"

All right, reader. Stop reading here. This is the way half the love stories of the world end.

Miss Bruce was trying to remember.

"There were so many," she said.

I let go her hand.

"Did you ever go to India?" I asked.

"India?" she replied. "Oh, you must be mistaken."

Christie street was only five blocks away now. She looked away, puzzling. She looked up at me, trying to recollect.

Christie street was coming up. I rang the bell cord. I reached down and took her hand again. I got off the car and had a little trouble seeing the curb.

Whatever you do, if you have a teacher who put you on the path, who showed you the way, who taught you not to be afraid, go find her, or him, go find them before it is too late.

Before they forget you.

Apparition at the Picnic

If ever the Connors, one of my across-the-road neighbours, invite you on a picnic, don't you hesitate. You go!

Theirs aren't any of these little picnic-basket affairs, with a few hard-boiled eggs, some stiff sandwiches and a couple of vacuum jugs.

They have a small trailer, painted dark green. It is about the size of two steamer trunks. It skims along behind their car, and you would never guess what it has inside. It has a fold-up barbecue outfit, bags of charcoal, tins of lighting fluid.

It has slices of tenderized ham half an inch thick, about the circumference of a grapefruit. It has mustard that Connor gets from a Chinese restaurant friend of his, beaten like whipped cream, and subtle as Satan himself.

"How's about a farewell to summer?" called Connor across the street. "We're going on a picnic tomorrow."

"Sold!" I cried.

Or if it isn't tenderized ham in that trailer, it might be little chunks of lamb about the size of a golf ball, mushrooms, tomatoes already quartered, and dainty folds of fat bacon. This would be for shishkabob or shashlik. They have half a dozen yard-long skewers, with wooden handles, for spearing these comestibles, each in its order, to be barbecued over the charcoal.

And onions! I forgot the onions. Every fourth piece on the skewer is a quarter of an onion! The purple variety for choice.

"My boss," called Connor, "the president of the company, has asked me to drop by his summer place to pick up an outboard motor he wants to give his nephew. So we're going to picnic in very exclusive surroundings."

"Whereabouts?" I asked (though I was thinking of either the ham steaks or the shashlik.)

"Lake Wikamog," called Connor. "About two hours. Pick you up around 9 A.M.?"

"O.K.," I said gratefully.

Now, potatoes, for example. The Connors take these big fat potatoes, grease them with butter, encase them in air-tight folds of aluminum foil. And these they put on the barbecue, when the charcoal is a beautiful ashy grey, the ruby red of the fire slumbering beneath. You never tasted such potatoes, when you unwrap them, baked, and their skins stiff as vellum, and you split 'em and put in a square of butter. It is like Columbus discovering America.

Or, Mrs. Connor, who is a Roman Catholic, will get some finnan haddie about two inches thick. I never see finnan haddie that big elsewhere. And I assure you that grilled finnan haddie, two inches thick, with whatever secret basting she puts on it as it grills, is one of the finest gifts of the Seven Seas of the World.

I was up at 7 A.M. and had a very light breakfast.

I was sitting on the front steps when Connor hailed me from his side drive to come and help him latch the trailer on.

"Can I help Mrs. Connor carry out the stuff?" I asked, when we had all snug.

"Oh, it's all packed," said Connor.

Which was a disappointment, as now I would have to wait until somebody brought up the subject.

I had not long to wait. Mrs. Connor and the two boys, ten and six, came out, and away we went. We had hardly left the city's limits when Mrs. Connor said:

"Well, we're having something different today."

"Yes?"

"A casserole," she said. "We've never had a casserole on a picnic. And this is a dandy."

"It's a . . ." began the younger boy.

"Sssshhh!" cut in Mrs. Connor. "It's a surprise."

"I think we might run into another surprise," said Connor at the wheel. "The radio said there were thunder storms up in the lake country, and by the look of that sky ahead . . ."

Low on the horizon stretched a dark band of cloud.

"Ah, well," said Mrs. Connor. "If it rains, we can have our picnic on the president's veranda."

My heart meanwhile had fallen a little bit. If there is anything that makes me tired, it's casserole. It is not flesh, fowl or good red herring. It is a limp dish, full of rice, dispirited meat and various sorts of goo. But I did not let my mind dwell on it.

Inside of an hour, we knew we were in for bad weather. By the time we got to the little village at the foot of Lake Wikamog, it was one of those steady all-day downpours.

We had to stop in the village at the cottage of the caretaker, to whom Connor had a note from the president to let us have the key to the boathouse.

"The house keys are on the ring too," said the elderly wife of the caretaker. "But don't go in there!"

"Certainly not," said Connor.

As soon as we drove out of hearing. Mrs. Connor's dander was up.

"Don't go in THERE!" she mimicked the old lady. "That's a nice way to talk to people! For all she knows, you might be the VICE-president."

We drove around the shore road to the gate of the lane, into the president's "summer place."

Even dripping in the rain, it was a beautiful house. It was a perfect copy of those lovely little houses you see in Quebec villages, with the sloping roof and the wide veranda.

Connor drove on to the gravel patio right alongside the veranda so we could all bail out without getting soaked.

"We'll set up the barbecue here," said Mrs. Connor.

"Fine," said Connor. "If the rain slacks off, I'll go down there to the boathouse and get the engine."

Mrs. Connor had the ring of keys still in her hand. She walked over to the door and inserted the key.

"Hey!" said Connor.

"I'm just going to have a peep," she said, pushing the door open.

We all had a peep. It was a magnificent room. A huge stone fireplace faced us. Long curtains, handloomed by the look of them, were drawn to, and swept down in tones of beige and pale yellow. On the shining hardwood floor were large round handicraft rugs in light colors.

"I've decided," said Mrs. Connor, throwing the door wide. "We're going to set up the barbecue in the fireplace!"

"Are you crazy?" asked Connor.

"What did the president say," she demanded, "when he asked you to pick up the engine?"

"Well," said Connor, "he said to have a nice picnic and explore the place . . ."

"Right!" said Mrs. Connor. "And if he knew we arrived in a thunder storm and a downpour, do you think he would mind if we set up the barbecue in that great big beautiful fireplace?"

She advanced toward it with that air women have for making an entrance.

Connor and I went and opened the trailer and carried in the barbecue and wicker basket with the mysteries in it; the folding table and camp chairs.

"Set the table on the veranda," directed Mrs. Connor. "We'll eat outside but we'll cook inside. That will prevent the boys from messing the place up. Stay out on the veranda, you boys!"

"What is it?" I hissed to Connor, as we carried the wicker basket inside. "What's a casserole, for Pete's sake?"

In a matter of minutes, Connor, skilled in these matters, had the barbecue set up and loaded with charcoal. Out of the wicker basket, shrouded with aluminum foil,

came the casserole.

"My brother in Saskatchewan," announced Mrs. Connor, "sent us four mallard wild ducks, by airmail express. They are in this casserole, with wild rice, and onions and certain other little things. It's already cooked. All we do now is heat it."

Connor took a can and squirted lighting fluid all over

the charcoal in the barbecue, lost in the width and depth of the lovely fireplace.

When he touched the match to it, there came a distant clattering, slithering, fluttering sound up the great stone chimney.

We stood bewitched.

As the flames leaped up, a monstrous black creature came tumbling down the chimney.

"A BAT!" screamed Mrs. Connor, leaping back.

The dread apparition flopped on to and off the barbecue all in one leap and came sailing into the room, banging on the floor, leaping into the air. It was no bat. It was as big as twenty bats.

On the handicraft rugs it left jet-black soot stains as big as a boot. The boys appeared in the open door, so the ebony evil monster flung itself against the long beige and yellow curtains, first the one on one side, then on the other, sliding down the curtains with streaks of soot behind it.

By now it was rid of enough soot for me to see what it was. It was a merganser. I caught a glimpse of its bill. So I lunged for it before it could commit further wreckage. I got it out the door, and it floundered off into the shrubbery.

Mrs. Connor had collapsed on one of the unsooted chesterfields. Connor grabbed the barbecue before it flamed too hot and rushed it out on to the veranda.

"What WAS it?" he gasped.

"A duck," I said. "A wild duck called a merganser."

Mrs. Connor appeared staggering in the doorway.

"What do we DOOOOOOOOOO?" she wailed.

❧

Connor drove back into the village and brought Mr. Perkins, the caretaker, and Mrs. Perkins came with him. And the whole thing was explained.

"After all," said Connor, "we are FRIENDS of the president. I am one of his executives."

"Aha?" speculated Mr. and Mrs. Perkins.

Anyway, Mrs. Connor put the casserole on the barbecue out on the veranda, while the rain came down in sheets. The odour of the mallard casserole wafted along and in the door where Mr. and Mrs. Perkins were taking down the curtains and rolling up the sooted rugs, and dusting up the dark spots on the hardwood floor.

"That darned merganser," said Mr. Perkins, coming out to stand around the casserole. "She nested this year and the year before in this chimney and I had to throw her out. So she nested in a stump along the shore here and raised a brood both times. But she had a sort of fix on this chimney here. Sort of hanging around. I got a shot at her last week and winged her. Probably she took cover in the chimney today on account of the weather . . . What have you got cooking here?"

The end was that for fifteen dollars Mrs. Perkins undertook to wash and rehang the curtains – a thing she had to do each year anyway – and clean the handicraft rugs and tidy everything up so that not a thing would show.

Then we all tucked into the casserole, the Perkinses and all.

Mr. Perkins went and helped Connor get the outboard.

"Not a word," said Connor, as we got in the car to drive away.

"Not a word," agreed Mrs. Perkins. "I shouldn't have let you have the house key in the first place."

So that was the famous Connor's wild-duck picnic which none of us will forget. The casserole changed my whole attitude toward casseroles.

And Connor learned that when your president invites you to kindly pick up an outboard motor for him, don't go prying around, no matter what your wife says.

There might be something up the chimney.

So We Tried
to Do It Ourselves

That windstorm Thursday night played havoc with the Wilsons' TV aerial across the street.

When I got up Friday morning and looked out the window to see what kind of a day it was, there was the aerial mast leaning drunkenly to the west.

I hurried to the phone and called Wilson.

"Yes, yes, I KNOW!" he interrupted me. "You're the eleventh person to call me. They started ringing the door-bell, even before seven o'clock."

Nothing upsets a neighbourhood so much as a TV aerial off kilter. Until you see one gone a little cockeyed, you don't realize how much these spidery additions to the urban landscape have contributed to modern architecture. It is better to neglect the painting of your home, better to forget to take the garbage cans in off the lawn, than to have a lopsided TV mast.

"Well," I said to Wilson, "I just thought I'd tell you."

"I know, I KNOW!" repeated Wilson, normally a most friendly man.

I realized he knew, of course. He has three children, from a teenager down to an eight-year-old. Therefore he has three TVs – a small one in his teenage daughter's room in the attic, the big one in the living room, and a medium one down in the rumpus room. The poor man.

When I got home for supper Friday evening, I was astonished to see Wilson's TV aerial still sagging to the west. No ladders in sight. No men scrambling around the roof.

When darkness fell, I couldn't resist giving Wilson a ring.

"I've spent the whole day," he said wearily, "trying to locate the people who sold me the aerial. About noon, I found out they had gone out of business. Bankrupt. So then I started to ferret out a guy I knew had been connected with the company. At four o'clock, I found out he had moved to California."

"Well," I protested, "they wouldn't guarantee the mast against a windstorm like Thursday night's, anyway."

"Nobody else's aerial was damaged!" declared Wilson. "Nobody in the whole block!"

"Are your TVs working all right?" I inquired.

"Listen!" said Wilson. "Can't you hear the kids howling and meowing and banging and stamping? NONE of the darned things work. They're all fuzzy. So the kids are going to visit neighbours for the evening."

The poor man.

Saturday morning, seeing Wilson and three or four of the neighbours gathered on his lawn staring up at the drunken mast, I went over and joined them.

"Clark," he said, "since eight this morning, I have called twenty TV aerial repair people. Most of them don't even answer. The ones that do answer, the ones that advertise 24-hour service in the yellow pages, all tell me they are booked up solid for the weekend, on account of the recent bad weather. The best offer I got is Tuesday. Tuesday! If possible!"

"Look," said Parker, who is our trigger man for the entire neighbourhood. "All we need is a handyman. There must be all sorts of handymen around who could come and straighten the darned thing. There's no great mystery about a TV aerial."

"Boys," I said, for I am much the oldest of the group, "the handyman vanished from our society forty or fifty years ago. There used to be two handymen in every village in the nation. There used to be ten or twenty in every town. There used to be one for every eight blocks in every city. But now, you'll never find one in the whole world."

Parker motioned us toward the Wilsons' front steps.

"Look," he said. "We'll call Morrison, over at the drug store. We'll call Chapman's, the butchers. They've been around here for years. They'll know somebody."

"Not a handyman," I assured them, as we sat down, the Wilson children staring moodily at us out the living-room window. "I remember Mr. Miles. We were one of his families. A handyman in each city district had his families. He could do plumbing. He could fix electric fixtures. He could build you a fence. He could lay concrete. He . . ."

But Parker signalled Wilson, and they went inside to telephone the druggist and the butcher. I reminisced to those who remained until the boys came out to say that neither Morrison nor the Chapmans knew of any handyman who could help straighten up a TV aerial.

"As a matter of fact," said Wilson, "Chapman's aerial was blown into his backyard Thursday night and he can't get anybody . . ."

"Look!" said Parker. "What's the matter with us? Why can't WE do it? What the heck is a handyman? He's a man who goes ahead and DOES things, without all this specialization, and trade unions, and off on weekends and stuff."

Some of us stood up.

"Look!" said Parker. "Old Whatsisname, around the corner here, has a big extension ladder. I've seen him rooting starling nests out of his eavetroughs. Clark, you can approach Whatsisname. He'll trust you."

"I'm no good at heights," said Connor.

"So long as I don't have to crawl out on the ridge," said Spencer.

"Clark," commanded Parker, "you go and borrow the ladder! I'll get some rope I brought down from the cottage. Who knows about electric wiring?"

"Well," said Wilson, "I'm pretty handy at wiring. So,

since it's my problem, after all, I'll go up and tie up any wiring that is loose. I've got lots of wire in the cellar."

Connor, Spencer and I went for the ladder. I had no trouble with Old Whatsisname. He is a rather unneighbourly neighbour. But I have a reverend air I can turn on. And when I explained the Christian nature of our errand, he led us to the ladder in his back yard.

"You will be responsible for it," he told me, formally.

By the time we got back with the ladder, Parker was already there with two large coils of rope. "Nylon," he said, "$\frac{1}{4}$-inch and $\frac{1}{2}$-inch. Strong enough to hold a bull elephant. I always bring it down from the cottage boathouse, along with my outboards, in case of break-ins."

Wilson had come up from the cellar with various coils of wire over his arms, a hammer, large nails, screws, and other tools projecting from his windbreaker pockets.

When we set up the extension ladder, of course, we had quite a gathering of the neighbours, and numerous children. Two young fellows passing in a small sports car backed up and parked and joined us. We therefore had plenty of help.

"I'm a sky diver," said one of the sports-car lads. "My chum and I will gladly go up on the roof."

So up they went, Parker first, with the ropes, then Wilson; then the two young strangers. Shouting instructions, Parker arranged a series of signals and prepared the ropes. He threw one end of the $\frac{1}{4}$-inch rope to the team in the Wilson side drive. The end of the $\frac{1}{2}$-inch rope he tossed down to the team in Miss McGillicuddy's side drive. Her house is next door east of Wilson's.

Miss McGillicuddy had taken up station out on her front lawn, an elderly lady well thought of by all the neighbourhood, including the children.

All was set. Parker did the shouting. The ropes were attached. Wilson stood ready, at the root of the trouble, with hammer, nails, screws, prepared to secure the plate that holds the mast erect.

From those who had withdrawn out to the sidewalk better to observe the performance, I have obtained the following particulars. To Parker's shouted commands, the team in Miss McGillicuddy's side drive hauled; and we on the Wilson's' side drive relaxed, a foot or two at a time.

Slowly, in jerks, the mast rose. And we on the ropes could tell by the applause out on the sidewalk that all was going well.

Parker's shouts became more commanding, more cautious. We on the ropes became more alert.

The mast reached the vertical. There was a cheer from the sidewalk.

Then, from various accounts, it seems the mast, with a gesture like that of a great opera singer coming to the end of an aria, having reached the climax, flung wide and went right over.

We on the Wilson end of the rope felt it burning through our hands. We bunched. We clung desperately.

But over went the mast, smash on to Miss McGillicuddy's gable on the side of her house.

It ripped off two yards of shingles from the gable, smashed the window frames to smithereens, crashed the glass to pieces, tore off fifteen feet of Miss McGillicuddy's eavetrough; and one malignant finger of Wilson's aerial could not resist snatching, for a final swipe, to tear off ten feet of Wilson's eastside eavetrough.

In the utter silence following the crash, there was only the one sound.

"Mercy!" said Miss McGillicuddy, out on her lawn.

Well, so much for handymen. From among the lot of us, we were able to scrounge up enough plywood and heavy cardboard to block up Miss McGillicuddy's gable windows.

"To keep the bats out," she said. "And I think I will spend Sunday with my sister, until Mr. Wilson . . . uh . . ."

It being now Saturday noon, all Wilson had to do was get somebody to re-erect his TV aerial, get a roofer to repair the shingles on Miss McGillicuddy's gable, a carpenter to repair the window frames, a glazier to repair the glass, and an eavetrough specialist to renew his and Miss McGillicuddy's eavetroughs.

Quite a chore for a Saturday noon.

Connor, Spencer and I dismantled and carried back Old Whatsisname's ladder.

We placed it exactly where Old Whatsisname directed us, against the fence.

"I trust," he said, "it proved of some use."

"Yes indeed," I lied.

The Mail Wouldn't
Go Through

When I came downstairs from my den with this big brown
envelope, all stamped and addressed, my womenfolk were
watching, seated in the living room.

"You're NOT," they said, "going OUT!"

Well, to tell the truth, it was slashing and sleeting, and
the wind was in the east.

"Just to the corner," I explained.

The letter box is only half a block west of my house.
The sleet was rattling on the windows.

"Don't," said my womenfolk, all getting up, "be CRAZY."

They came over, pretending to help me find my topcoat in the clothes closet.

When they saw the envelope, there was a unanimous
decision.

"THAT," they said, "will never go in a letter box!"

"I'll stuff it in," I assured them, gulfing into my topcoat.

They picked the envelope off the hall table.

"That will NEVER," they said, handing it to one another,
"NEVER go in a letter box! You'd have to walk all the way
over to that parcel box. Three blocks!"

"Oh, I'll stuff it in all right," I assured them as I reached
for the envelope and opened the front door.

The blast of wind nearly pulled the door knob from
my hand.

Sleet swished in.

"There!" cried my womenfolk. "You're CRAZY to go
out!"

I closed the door.

"Darlings," I explained quietly. "I promised my editor that this would be in the mail tonight. Sunday. The only pickup is at 5 P.M. on Sunday. It is now fifteen minutes to five."

"Your editor," they replied, "would rather get your story late than have you die of pneumonia."

"You don't know editors," I informed them.

And tucking my neck in my collar and my head well into my hat, I stepped forth.

I kept the envelope under my coat. The gale was in the east, therefore dribbling rain down the back of my neck as I walked the short half block to the letter box. The sleet was flying horizontally.

On reaching the box on its lamp post, I drew the envelope from under my coat, lifted the iron flap of the letter box and inserted the far end.

It was a tight fit, I pushed. It went in part way.

I waggled it carefully from side to side. It went in half way. Then more than half way. Then, with a final squash, it went nearly all the way except for about one inch.

And there it stuck. No matter how I shoved, it would go no farther.

I decided to pull it out and try again.

But it wouldn't come out. With only the inch left for me to grip and that inch already getting a little damp from the sleet, I pulled and teased and cautiously cajoled.

It was jammed fast.

Hearing something behind me, I turned. It was a woman with an umbrella, teetering in the gale. She was covered from head to foot in a fashionable rain slicker. In one hand, she held a bunch of letters.

"What's the matter?" she asked.

"Somebody," I said "SOMEBODY has tried to stick an oversize envelope in, and it's jammed the slot."

"Here," said the woman, handing me her letters. "Hold these a minute and I'll give it a shove."

She was about forty, and I noted that she had the cool commanding blue-eyed presence of a Rosedale resident.

She shoved. It only bunched up more.

"We'll pull it out," she said.

And with a firm jerk, she tore off a large piece of the now quite moist brown envelope.

"Serves them right, whoever they are," said she.

An elderly man with a wobbling umbrella came and joined us.

"What goes on?" he demanded indignantly.

We explained that somebody had jammed an oversize letter in the box.

"By jove!" he said. "That's interfering with Her Majesty's mail! Pull the damn thing out!"

"We've tried," we explained.

He being a large old man, and the woman and I being small, he said to me:

"Here, hold this a second."

I took his umbrella. With both hands, he got a firm grip on the bedraggled remnant of the envelope and heaved.

Off came another chunk of the brown envelope, and a little of the white sheets it enclosed.

"Shove it in," I suggested.

But it just bunched up more.

"Well," said the old man, heaving a sigh. "Of all the fatheads! Who in this neighbourhood would do a thing like this? I've got two very important letters . . ."

"Look, gentlemen," said the blue-eyed woman, "I've got a bunch of letters that HAVE to catch this mail. There is one of these big parcel-letter boxes three blocks over from here. If you will excuse me, I am a good deal younger than either of you; and I'm better dressed against the weather than either of you. So, if you will give me your letters, I'll take them over to the big box."

"That's mighty sporting of you!" exclaimed the big man, fighting his waggling umbrella. And he reached inside his coat and handed over his two letters. He waved goodbye and walked off.

The woman held the letters in her umbrella hand, well up to the handle, and held the other hand out to me.

What could I do?

I just stood there and stared at her. I have no doubt confusion showed in my face.

She glanced at the letter box, then back at me, a sardonic Rosedale smile growing on her face.

"Well, well, WELL!" she said.

She turned and walked off toward the three blocks to the parcel-letter box.

I looked at my watch. It was now 10 past five. How time flies!

I decided to wait for the red Royal Mail pickup car.

Several passing cars in the sleet paused when they saw me. Two of them ran down their window to ask if I was all right.

"Thank you, yes," I called back cheerily. But I decided to walk up and down, a little way, rather than just stand there by the letter box.

Thank heavens, no more letter posters came before the red car arrived, at 5:25.

"This manuscript of mine," I explained to the driver, as he leaped out with his bag and keys, "got stuck in the slot, and I'd like it back."

He studied the situation, after opening the box door.

"According to regulations," he said, scooping the letters into his bag. "I can't let you have this back, because it is IN the box, really."

"Look," I said, "it's been damaged, trying to get it out. If I identify myself . . ."

"Oh, I know you, Mr. Clark," said the driver. "I was staying at the same motel as you last summer, when we were fishing . . ."

So I opened up the brown envelope, which he easily pulled free from inside the box, to show him.

"It's irregular," said he. "But o.k."

We shook hands, and I faced into the east gale and sleet and walked the half block home.

My womenfolk were watching out the living-room and dining-room windows for me. They ran to open the door.

"Where on earth have you BEEN?" they cried. "We were just going to call the police."

(As you grow older, they treat you like a baby.)

They were helping me out of my sodden clothes.

There was my envelope, sadly wrecked.

"So you DIDN'T go all the way over to the parcel box!" they said.

"No, I met a couple of people and had a chat," I explained.

"You must be off your rocker," they concluded.

They took my topcoat and hat to rang up to dry in the kitchen and I took my soggy manuscript back up to my den.

There I tore it, and its carbon copy included, into small pieces, and sat down and wrote THIS story instead.

(P.S. This story arrived in time –
Editor.)

Ring Around a Rosies

In the year 1848, my grandmother Louisa McMurray was four years old. She was playing *Ring Around a Rosies* with her three older sisters, one older brother Tom, and her baby brother, Little Robert.

Over the picket fence came this dog.

All houses in Toronto in those days had picket fences to keep out the cows, pigs and poultry that wandered about. The McMurray house was on the south side of King street, west of St. Lawrence Market, and almost kit-a-corner from St. James Church, now the cathedral.

The children were yelling and laughing:

> *"Ring around a rosies*
> *A pocket full of posies*
> *Who squats down FIRST!"*

And whoever was slowest to squat had to stand in the middle while the other children, holding hands, danced around in the ring.

The dog came over the picket fence.

It seized Little Robert and killed him.

Right before the eyes of the horrified children, the dog took Little Robert and shook him and killed him.

Of course, neighbours came; and they shot the dog, which belonged to the Allan family that later gave the land for Allan Gardens in the old heart of Toronto, where there is a beautiful horticultural garden and greenhouses; and where the beatnik poets gather to read their poems; and local Nazis try to make their speeches.

Now, in 1848 they knew little or nothing about rabies,

or hydrophobia. Mad dogs. That was all they knew. Louis Pasteur, in France, was only 26, with all his miracles ahead of him.

But one thing they knew nothing whatever about is what the psychologists now call trauma. That is a startling experience that has a lasting effect on the mind. Louisa had hold of Little Robert's hand when the dog tore him away. And all her eighty-five years, my grandmother lived in quiet terror of dogs.

Her seventh and youngest child was my mother, Sarah Louise. Everybody knew she had inherited Louisa's terror. My aunts, uncles, family friends, my father, all knew Sarah Louise both feared and hated dogs. The curse was being handed on.

She was nineteen years old when I was born on September 25, 1892. In prim and proper Toronto in the early Nineties, young pregnant women did not walk abroad, as they do today, carrying their burden proudly before them and looking everybody bung in the eye. No. In 1892, they tried to keep the stork theory intact, and after the sixth or seventh month, they went out only after dusk. My father, Joe Clark, a young newspaper editor, hurried home the evening of September 24; and after supper, as soon as it grew dark, and the lamplighter came up and around Mackenzie Crescent with his four-foot lighting stick, to turn on the gas street lamps every 100 yards or so, my father took Sarah Louise out for their nightly constitutional.

It was dark and silent. No traffic. After supper, all the delivery carts were tucked home in their stables. Nobody had porch lights There were no side drives, of course. Only narrow side entrances between the houses.

Out of one of these side entrances, howling bloody murder, came a large dog. Somebody had apparently caught it at the garbage pail and given it a boot or a brick.

It raced howling right in the path of my parents.

My mother fainted. In response to my father's shouts, neighbours came hurrying out from their supper. They helped carry my mother back home. At noon next day, Sunday (and Sunday's child is full of grace, and with Libra just coming into the Zodiac, promising all sorts of good fortune, according to all my aunts gathered for the occasion), I was born.

They were fearful for me. They were happy to see I bore no purple birthmarks in the shape of a dog across my face. Old wives' tales were part of daily life in 1892.

You did not put a baby out in winter, on the front stoop. By April, I was able to sit up in my new white wicker baby carriage, with its dangling pale green silk parasol. (I remember it, for my brothers and sister occupied it in turn.) And hardly had I been put out, in the spring sunshine, before my screams brought my mother and whatever aunts were in the house – in 1893 you always had country-town aunts visiting the big city of Toronto (pop. 170,699) on shopping trips from Seaforth, Clinton, Pickering and more distant points. And there I was, purple in the face and screaming. A dog was rambling nearby.

They rushed me indoors. It was true! It was true!

I had inherited the tragic memory of Little Robert.

Thereafter, they put me out on the back steps, with the side-entrance gate securely latched. When I could toddle, I was always picked up swiftly if a dog appeared. When I grew too big to be snatched up, I was discreetly brought to heel, close to my father's or my mother's legs, on the far side, if a dog hove by. Of such things are myths of life derived.

My father, Joe Clark, ostensibly a Presbyterian, out of family and social considerations, was really a rationalist, as I found out in time. To him, all this stuff about old wives' tales and inherited fears was nonsense.

On my fifth birthday, at breakfast, I was seated, in honour of the fact that I was the heir to the headship of the family, in my father's armchair at the head of the dining-room table. This was a great and traditional hon-our. My birthday presents, all white tissue and ribbons, were spread before me. The family, consisting of Louisa, my grandmother, and various aunts, and Bella, the maid, were assembled. My father kept popping in and out of the kitchen with a strangely conspiratorial air. When I had opened all my gifts – and you may say a child of five cannot remember that far back, but one of them was a fire engine with two black horses that leaped up and down as you drew them, hauling a scarlet and nickle-plated fire engine – and sat back in pride and triumph, my father appeared from the kitchen.

In his arms he carried something small and black.

He came and placed in my arms – Bonnie!

A tiny, jet-black cocker spaniel six weeks old. I remem-ber this. I remember looking down at him. With his bleary puppy eyes he looked up at me. He licked the bottom of my chin.

I closed my arms around him.

And so died the myth.

Bonnie lived three years, when he was killed in a dog fight. I have not seen a dog fight in forty years; but in the 1890s, dog fights were a part of the normal day. Going to and from school in a week, you would see four or five. They were part of the entertainment of that era. The Calder boys, my chums, helped me carry Bonnie back home. It was, of course, tragic. After a few days, my Grandma Louisa told my parents that I was obviously going into a decline. Going into a decline was one of the more familiar ailments. I grieved for Bonnie. It is not easy to measure the grief of a child for a dog.

The first dog my father could get to replace Bonnie was a greyhound, named Flirt, from one of his sporting friends. She was mouse-grey, slender as a pencil, and higher in the rump than in the shoulder. She was not cuddleable. She did not last long. Grandma Louisa staged one of her cookie-baking sprees, the savour of which spread half a block in all directions and all the children foregathered for the handout. By then, I had a young brother Joe, aged five. Joe was born with a sense of indignation. When we lined up for the cookies, Joe got one, which he held behind him in his left hand, and got in line for another. Flirt came up behind him and snatched the hidden cookie.

Joe grabbed a paring knife from the kitchen table, seized Flirt by the tail and tried to cut her long snake-like tail off. Flirt, with her mouth full of cookie, turned and yelped, and Grandma Louisa, holding her apron bravely before her, rescued Joe and shooed Flirt from the house. Joe was not only born indignant. He was unforgiving. He could not forget that cookie. And for days, every time Flirt came within reach, Joe would try to give her a kick in the slats (which is a good description of a greyhound, come to think of it!) or punch her in the nose. And at last Flirt bared her teeth at Joe. That settled it. Away she went back to the country, where she could course rabbits instead of cookies.

Our next dog was an English bulldog, Ben Stone, a pudgy little brindled puppy that grew, month by month, into the most frightening character you ever saw. His face wrinkled in an expression of incredulity, two fangs of his lower jaw protruding, white and naked, from under his upper lip. Bow-legged, barrel-chested, massive, the kindest dog we ever owned. My baby sister, Mabel, used to grab his ridiculous kinky tail and drag him backward, sliding over the linoleum kitchen floor. And Ben Stone would waggle his huge head from side to side in sheer delight at the discovery of such an amusing game. Ben died of distemper at the age of two.

Next came an Irish terrier named Rory O'More. He was a fighting Irishman. Up at Georgian Bay each summer, he could find more skunks, porcupines and Massasauga rattlesnakes than any dog is entitled to. No matter how many quills we pulled from his face, back he went to find another porky. He smelt of skunk for weeks after we got home to the city.

"No more dogs!" said my mother, at the end of the third summer. "No more DOGS!"

So my father gave Rory O'More to the farmer who, every Friday, called at our house with eggs, butter and vegetables.

And then went out and bought Bonnie Two!

Like Bonnie One, he came into the house at the age of six weeks. He lived with us for eleven years, and a more beautiful, intelligent dog we never had. He could speak English. Well, at least he could understand it. He had a natural sense of the duty of a dog. When my parents went to the theatre or to a party and locked up the house, after sending us children to bed, Bonnie would go downstairs and lie in the vestibule, on guard, until they came home. At Georgian Bay, he never tangled with a skunk or porcupine, but, at a respectful distance, would summon aid in the form of a .22 rifle. He had a special bark for rattlesnakes; and when he found one, his high-hysterical barking brought us with paddles or rakes to find him circling the snake at four feet, confusing it and keeping it from escaping.

He was the only dog we ever had that my mother really patted. All our other dogs, if they came up to her, she would reach down, as if to pat them. But we knew she was really pushing them away.

Ah, we had a whole five years of beagles, I owned thirteen of them at one time – boarded out on a farm, of course. But then I had to go to war; and without me, my young sons lost interst, and we gave the beagles away to fellow beaglers.

Then Dolly, a black-and-white cocker, the stupidest silliest dog I ever knew, who knew what I thought of her, and only came to me in thunderstorms to hide behind my feet, knowing I would protect her from this awful menace.

And Knuckles, a red cocker. And Chelsea, a corgi.

A galaxy of dogs. You may wonder why I titled this story *Ring Around a Rosies*. It is this.

"Oft in the stilly night, ere slumber's chains have bound me, fond memory brings" – not the light of other days, but a company of the ghosts of all the little dogs whom I have known and who knew me. Not one at a time, mind you. But all together, from Bonnie One, all through Ben Stone and Bonnie Two and Dolly and Knuckles and twenty more, right up to the last, who was Chelsea.

And in my mind, I let the little ghosts form a Ring Around a Rosies. And it is fun.

And I know what they are doing. They are making amends, as they frolic in the silence of dreams, to Louisa, my grandmother.

The Private World
of Milly Pierce

I will bet you anything you like that within twenty-five years (by which time I won't be here to collect) the most precious thing on this earth will not be diamonds or rubies, or gold, pure gold.

No. The most precious thing on earth will be privacy.

You remember those little horse-shoe-shaped magnets, painted red, we used to get in our Christmas stockings? With each magnet came a small packet of iron filings. You scattered the iron dust over the table and then slowly edged the magnet toward it.

The way the filings raced to the magnet is the way humanity today is racing toward the cities. The way the filings piled on top of each other, creating a sort of fur, is the way we humans are piling on top of each other in the cities and suburbs.

Privacy is unthinkable. The so-called mass media of TV, radio and a press, whose rumble never ceases day or night, leave nothing undisclosed. If we try to flee away to some wilderness hideaway, we find the highways bumper to bumper with us, all headed the same way, in the same hope. And when we get there, there is no room to park.

These were the thoughts that were occupying my mind as I walked in the thronged tall handsome corridors of the big department store, where I bumped right into Milly Pierce.

She looked awful.

"Milly!" I exclaimed, taking her hand and leading her

out of the trampling multitude of the big store, over to the wall.

"Oh, Greg. I'm in the worst mess!" said Milly.

She looked it.

"What has happened?" I asked.

I should tell you, right here, that nothing much should happen to Milly Pierce. When her husband, Pete Pierce, died three years ago, he left her very well off indeed – stocks, bonds, apartment houses, real estate, trust funds: all sorts of loot. She was the envy of all the women who knew her. Not a chick nor child, nor any close kin to bother her.

I looked at her now, her hair out of control, looking as if she had got up out of bed in a hurry and rushed out.

That, of course, is exactly what she had done.

"What's happened?" I demanded.

"Greg, you couldn't believe it," she said. "The idiot in the apartment above mine, on the next floor, left his bath running all night, and when I woke this morning . . . !"

Milly waved her hands.

"The water had seeped in around the windows," she said, "and at the edges of walls. All the lovely silk wall covering in my living room was wilted off. My paintings, the water colours and drawings, ruined. My furniture soggy. My rugs sopping!"

"What are you doing right now?" I asked briskly.

"On my way to the insurance-company office," she said.

"O.K.," I said, "but get a lawyer. Get a lawyer too."

"Lawyer!" said Milly. "After what Pete's lawyers did to me over his estate, I don't SPEAK to lawyers."

"Listen, darling," I insisted. "Get a lawyer. There will be all kinds of complications. Your insurance will have what they call deductibles, and little-print clauses. The idiot in the apartment above you will be involved, and so will the apartment house."

"I own half the apartment house," put in Milly.

"All the more reason you must have a lawyer," I assured

her. "By the way, where DO you live?"

I had lost touch with Milly after Pete Pierce died. For a very simple reason. Milly did not approve of me. I was one of the gang who took her husband Pete away fishing or hunting. We took Pete on tackle- or gun-buying trips to New York. We were a bad lot. For Milly, being childless, wanted Pete for HER little boy. And we were the unprincipled rascals who persuaded him he was a man.

Milly named her apartment house, which I didn't know.

"I'm sorry to have lost touch with you, Milly," I said, "But you know . . ."

"I have an unlisted telephone," said Milly, drily.

But she was obviously glad to have run into me to find a little sympathy.

"Well, I must trot along," she said, pushing her hair back.

"And don't forget to get a lawyer!" I repeated sternly.

"I don't know one," she said. "I don't SPEAK to Pete's lawyers."

"Well, heck," I said, "Jimmie Henderson is a good one. He looks after me."

"Was he one of Pete's pals?"

"No, no," I assured her. "He's a quiet old bachelor; reads a lot, goes to the ballet; that sort."

"How do I get him?"

"His firm is Smith, Henderson, Smith, Smith and Mc-Conkey," I said. "Here, I'll write it down for you."

I wrote the firm name on a bit of paper from my pocket.

"Well," said Milly, dismissing me.

"Now, DO call me and tell me how things work out," I said, patting her arm. "You will be in a mess for days or weeks, I suppose. Give me a ring, and I'll take you to lunch."

"Thanks, Greg," she said, "but I live pretty quietly, now. I LOVED my apartment . . . !"

Tears came in her eyes as she turned and walked off into the swirling throng.

When I got home at 6 P.M., there was a strange telephone number for me to call. I dialled, and it was Milly.

"Greg, you will never believe what happened!"

"What?"

"When I got through at the insurance company, where it turned out I had all the wrong kinds of insurance for this particular case, I called your Mister Henderson."

"Yes?"

"I went to see him and told him my story," said Milly, with gasps. "I gave him all my insurance-company papers and my apartment deeds and stuff. And do you know what?"

"What?"

"He," said Milly, "is the IDIOT upstairs who left the bathtub on."

"Aw, come ON, Milly!"

"You should have seen him blush!" cried Milly. "I haven't seen a man blush for years and years. I called him an IDIOT before I knew who . . ."

"But, Milly," I protested, "did Jimmie Henderson just move in to your apartment house? Didn't you know him?"

"He lived in the apartment house before I moved in three years ago," said Milly, "before I bought a half interest in it."

"But you mean you never . . . ?" I asked incredulously.

"OF COURSE not!" said Milly. "Have you ever lived in an apartment house?"

"Never!" I said piously.

"Well, you NEVER know anybody else in an apartment house," explained Milly. "Where would your PRIVACY be, if you did?"

Privacy!

When I heard her use the word, I could feel my psyche starting to jiggle inside of me. My psyche always begins to jiggle when strange things are starting to happen.

"But surely . . ." I said.

"Look, Greg," said Milly. "When you live in an apartment house, and you come out of your suite for the elevator, and you see one of your neighbours in the corridor closer to the elevator than you, you always stop, pretend you have forgotten your gloves, and you turn around and go back to your apartment. Then you peek out and, when they have gone down, YOU go out."

"Milly, I can't believe you!"

"It's true," she said. "When you get in the elevator and there are people from upper floors in it, you don't raise your eyes."

"Milly!"

"It's true," she said. "Anyway, I want to thank you for steering me on to Mr. Henderson. He says everything will be looked after, and I'll be all cleaned up in jig time. In a week, he says!"

When she hung up, I had to sit for a minute before my psyche stopped jiggling.

At around 8 P.M. Jimmie Henderson phoned.

"Greg, I want to thank you for sending a young lady to see me this noon, a Mrs. Pierce."

(Young lady? Milly is forty-six.)

"But Jimmie, is it ethical," I asked, "for you to take her case, when you are involved?"

"Oh, yes," said Jimmie. "I have looked at it from all angles."

"I am told," I said, "that you blush."

"Well, she called me an idiot," said Jimmie, with a strange sound in his voice.

Ah, you know the end of the story already.

Six weeks later, Jimmie Henderson, who is fifty-two, a dedicated bachelor, and not much given to social activities, invited me to tea at his apartment at 4 P.M. on Sunday.

Tea!

When I got there, I found it was a beautiful high-rise

apartment house in a whole fashionable neighbourhood of high-rise apartments. There was nobody in sight when I got out of the taxi. The whole area seemed to be uninhabited. If I ever saw privacy, here it was.

When I entered the apartment's regal doors, a uniformed doorman looked at me stonily.

"Mr. Henderson?" I said meekly.

"Six," said the doorman, with the warmth of a computer.

Jimmie Henderson's apartment was beautiful – a study full of law books as prim and stately as a court of law; a living room with two walls given over to a hi-fi player, out of which, soft and muted, was coming Act Four of the *Nutcracker*. And it was just when the *Pas de Deux* rose from it, sweeping, glorious, Jimmie Henderson said:

"Greg, I have asked you here to tell you something. Milly and I are engaged to be married!"

So THAT was what made my psyche jiggle? As if I didn't know.

We then went downstairs one floor to Milly's apartment, where we had Sunday tea. And her apartment was beautiful, the walls all newly done in softly-flowered silk instead of wall paper or paint; and the furniture was like a stage setting in an Arthur Wing Pinero society drama in the time of King Edward VII.

Next Friday, I have a curious task. I am to go down to one of those places where you rent formal costumes. Despite my shape, I am to be fitted with a morning coat and striped trousers, a grey tie such as I have never owned in my life, either, and a shirt with turn-down corners on the separate collar.

And I have an unusual role. The wedding on Saturday is to be in the vestry of Milly's church. Jean Sutherland is to be the matron of honour.

I am to play two parts.

At first, I will stand by the side of Jimmie Henderson, as his best man.

Then, at the right moment, when the parson asks "Who gives this woman in marriage?" I am to step smartly to the left, beside Milly, and say:

"I do."

They are going on a world cruise for their honeymoon, to the Mediterranean and the Isles of Greece, where burning Sappho loved and sang. And I know exactly what will happen. Before they are decently settled in their de luxe cabin, a social hostess of the great ship will turn up and wheedle and cajole and charm them.

And there they will be, in evening dress, in the crowded ballroom of the lovely ship, being bumped and jostled just as Milly and I were in the lofty corridors of the big department store the day I was ruminating on privacy.

I am, as you see, a philosopher, especially in the field of the explosion of the human population.

And I am beginning to come to the conclusion that the human species doesn't WANT privacy.

The Fish That
Got Around

It was bedtime when the phone rang. It was long distance.

"Put in ninety cents," I heard the operator say.

And as I listened to the clank-clank, tinkle-tinkle, I already knew it was from The Big Dam.

"Greg," shouted my fishing companion Bill Davis. "Guess what!"

"What?" I guessed.

"I got a TWENTY-NINE-POUND, TEN-OUNCE lake trout at the Dam!"

"You're kidding!" I protested.

"Right after supper," shouted Davis, because the long-distance phone from The Big Dam is kind of primitive. "I went down to that fast water below the Dam with that little five-ounce spinning outfit. A couple of Americans had got two or three nice pound, pound-and-a-half speckled trout there earlier in the day. Well, sir . . ."

"What in the world," I cut in, "would a LAKE trout be doing in there?"

(The lake trout, called grey trout in many parts of this country, is usually found in deep lakes and around their shores in spring and fall.)

"It must have come up all the way from Pot Lake," said Bill.

"Six miles," I figured. "Upstream? What shape was it in?"

"Perfect!" exulted Davis. "I'm going to have it mounted. I just thought I'd give you a ring and you could spread the word around among the boys."

"Got any pictures of it?" I inquired, being a news-paperman.

"No, it was just dark by the time we landed it," said Davis. "I had half the village and all the tourists for an audience, after an hour on that six-pound monofilament line. I've got the fish in Mr. McDermott's freezer."

Mr. McDermott is the proprietor of the general store at The Big Dam, the only store serving quite a large cottage community up the lakes.

"When are you coming down?" I asked.

"Next weekend," said Davis. "And you might check up for me where the best place is to get it mounted. And how much."

"I'll do that," I said. "And congratulations."

"I'm getting plenty," agreed Davis. "Everybody for miles around has been into the village to see the trout."

We said goodnight just in time as the operator said, "Your three minutes are up."

That was Saturday night. Sunday noon, Davis was on the phone again.

"Where are you?" I asked, astonished.

"In town," said Davis. "I've got to go to Chicago. Early this morning the head office got me on long distance. And they ordered me to get to Chicago in time for a meeting Monday with our American company to explain the Canadian tax structure. . . ."

"Where's the fish?" I demanded, some things being more important than others.

"I left it in Mr. McDermott's freezer," said Davis. "I'll bring it down next weekend. I didn't want it lying around here on a Sunday, without anybody knowing . . ."

"I'd have looked after it," I assured him.

"Well, I have to catch the 4 P.M. plane," said Davis, "and it was all of a fluster anyway. So I thought I'd just leave it with Mr. McDermott until next weekend. It will be o.k."

And then he gave me a fresh play-by-play account of how he caught the monster, and who helped him land it on the rocks down at the foot of the Dam. It was a great battle.

Tuesday, Belle, who is Bill Davis's wife, called me long distance.

"Have you heard from Bill?" she asked.

"No, he said he wouldn't be back until tomorrow."

"Well, they're catching an awful lot of whopping big trout at the Dam," she said.

"Oh?"

"Yes," she said. "Didn't you see Mr. McDermott's picture in the paper?"

"NO!"

"He got one every bit as big as Bill's." said Belle. "Right at the foot of the Dam. Tell Bill, if he calls you."

When I hung up, I went and got the morning paper. I never look at the sports pages. But there was Mr. McDermott.

Four columns.

He was standing at the foot of the Dam, right at the edge of the white water, holding his rod high in one hand, and with the other lifting a magnificent great lake trout, turned so its shining side caught the light.

I put the paper carefully aside for Bill when he got back from Chicago.

He didn't get back until Friday. Those Americans are very hard to explain the Canadian tax structure to.

I agreed to go up to The Big Dam with him for the weekend and help him bring the fish home, and also his family, who don't go up until July.

I showed him Mr. McDermott's beautiful picture in the paper.

He studied it intently.

He read the heading over the photo and the lines under it: "Popular Lakeland Merchant Makes Big Catch."

"Mr. Adolphus McDermott, well-known general-store

keeper at The Big Dam, lands a record-breaking lake trout. . . ."

Then there were a few more lines describing Mr. Mc-Dermott's struggles with the fish.

"Hmmmm!" said Davis, studying the picture more intently.

And all the three-hour drive to The Big Dam, he kept saying "Hmmm," though I tried to take his mind off it.

At Fordbridge, which is the last town on the highway where you turn off on the side road to The Big Dam, we pulled into Bert's Service Station.

"Well, by golly," said Bert, coming out himself instead of letting the boy serve us. "Did YOU ever start something!"

"How do you mean?" asked Davis.

"Why, there must be a SHOAL of those big lake trout at The Big Dam, like you got," said Bert. "Wait a minute!"

He went back into the station and came out with a coloured snapshot.

"I begged this," said Bert proudly, "off an American gentleman going out Wednesday. I'm going to get the town council to get colour prints of it and we'll distribute them everywhere."

The snapshot — one of those done-in-a-minute kind — was of a pot-bellied sportsman standing in the now familiar position at the foot of the Dam. In one hand holding high a small spinning rod and in the OTHER its tail dragging in the white water, an enormous lake trout.

"THIRTY pounds!" said Bert. "Man, if this doesn't start another Klondyke rush into this region! Did you see old McDermott's picture in the city papers?"

"Yes," said Davis, giving him back the colour print.

We drove in the side road to The Big Dam, twenty miles.

"Hmmmm!" said Davis, over and over. "Hmmmm!"

We drove straight to Mr. McDermott's store when we reached The Big Dam. As usual, it was brightly lighted and crowded with the early-season cottagers and the local inhabitants glad to see summer coming again. Mr. Mc-Dermott did not see us until we were right in front of him at the cheese counter, where he was cornering off a beautiful hunk of genuine Cheddar.

Mr. McDermott reeled back.

"Hah! Mr. Davis!" said he, a little breathless.

"I'd like," said Davis, "to see my fish."

"Of course, of course, of COURSE!" said Mr. McDermott, entirely ignoring the woman who was buying the lovely Cheddar.

He cleared his throat and led us to the back of the crowded store to the shed where he keeps his freezer, bigger than two coffins, and his two refrigerators. (We have electricity at The Big Dam, naturally.)

We followed. Mr. McDermott lifted the lid of the freezer. He groped around among the contents. On a great sheet of brown oiled paper, he lifted out the trout and held it toward Davis.

"Hello!" said a jovial voice from the entrance. "Is this the FISH?"

He was a pot-bellied sportsman. He thrust himself into our midst and let out a roar of approval.

"I've got a friend out in front," he bellowed, "with a strobe-light camera. Can we get down to the white water at this time of night? Ten bucks, is it?"

Mr. McDermott said:

"Aw, awah, aw, I . . . uh . . . awah . . ."

It was a sorry-looking fish. Its gill covers gaped wide, as if from many a trip down to the bottom of the Dam. Its fins were frayed, its tail worn away on the edges.

I felt called upon to do something.

"Excuse me," I said, "but there is a little DEAL going on here. I wonder would you mind . . . ?"

And I ushered the sportsman to the shed door, back into the store.

"Look, Mr. Davis," said Mr. McDermott. "When you

went out last Sunday, you stopped in at Bert's Service Station and told him what you had. Didn't you?"

"Yes," admitted Bill stiffly.

"Inside of an hour, that young fellow," said Mr. Mc-Dermott, "who works on the Fordbridge weekly, comes in with a camera. He wanted a picture of the fish. He got me to pose. The NEXT thing I knew, that PICTURE was in the city papers! I didn't know WHAT to do!"

"Well, you got a few tourists," suggested Davis. "TEN bucks a pose?"

"Look, Mr. Davis. I remember every one of them! I'll give you the money . . ."

"MISTER McDermott!" said Davis, exactly like Captain Bligh in *Mutiny On The Bounty*.

He started out of the shed.

"The fish?" said Mr. McDermott, crushed.

"Cut it up," said Davis, "and give it to the poor."

And we stalked out.

When we got the four miles to Bill's cottage, Belle was waiting for us, full of laughter. She knew all about it.

"Bill," she said, after they had hugged, "I don't want any stuffed FISH! We've got moose antlers. We've got stuffed deer heads. Look! We've got stuffed partridge! We've got stuffed . . ."

But Davis shut her off with another hug.

"Nobody," he said, dismissing the whole thing. "NOBODY can steal from me the memory of the fight I had with that trout in that white water below the dam. Nobody!"

He looked very proud.

"You should have brought it down with you last Sunday," said I, "and I would have looked after it."

"I'm glad I didn't," replied Bill. "It is more FUN this way, and will stay a long time in our minds."

The Mystery of the Moulting Polar Bear

One thing George H. McCaul treasures above all his other valuables is a huge polar bear rug that carpets his library.

It is more than eleven feet long, more than seven feet wide, and a gorgeous snow white, except for a tinge of cream colour across the mane, or shoulders.

When I visit McCaul's library, I always step reverently around the rug, instead of trampling on it.

"Greg," said McCaul on the phone, "what do you know about bugs?"

"Bugs?" said I, astonished.

"Back at high school," said McCaul, "you used to collect butterflies, moths, bugs, grasshoppers . . ."

"Aw," I remembered, tenderly, those far-off days.

"Something is *eating* my polar bear rug!"said McCaul.

"*Eating* it?" I cried.

"Yes," said McCaul. "Something is taking snips and bites out of it. I've had a fur dealer up to look at it. I paid him $25 for the visit. And *he* couldn't figure it out."

"Did he mention dermestid beetles?" I enquired. "Called bacon beetles? They are the terror of museums and collectors . . ."

"Yes," said McCaul, "he mentioned them. He says for $50 he can come back with some kind of stripping comb they have and smooth the whole thing out, so the bites that have been taken won't show. But I don't want to do that until I know what the Sam Hill is eating it."

"Naturally," I said, though McCaul is a wealthy man to whom $50 is peanuts.

"Knowing how you love that rug," said he, "I thought if you were passing by some evening, you could drop in and have a look."

"Tonight!" I said promptly.

Because among other things in McCaul's library is a first edition of Capt. John Franklin RN's *Narrative Of A Voyage To The Polar Sea*, published in 1823. And to fondle such treasures, I would walk a hundred miles.

I walked around the block.

McCaul turned on the library lights full, and we knelt down on the rug while he showed me the curious bites out of the beautiful fur. Mind you, McCaul did not shoot this gorgeous creature. McCaul wouldn't shoot anything. He won't even fish.

He has become rich by investing in the mining market. I mean investing. He isn't one of those gamblers who sit in the stockbroker's offices watching the ticker tape float by up along the ceiling. No, sir! He puts on old clothes, flies to the immediate vicinity of a mining boom, hangs around Chinese restaurants (they are always the first social accommodation in mining booms) and around beer parlours. There he gathers from the horse's mouth the information upon which he invests in a mining stock.

It was in Yellowknife, N.W.T., that an Eskimo, shy at being so far south, stopped him on the street and asked if he would like to buy a polar bear hide.

"How much?" asked McCaul.

"Twenty-five dollar."

He went with the Eskimo to a shanty at the far end of town and there the gorgeous pelt was unwrapped from its ropes. It was not tanned, of course, just the raw pelt. McCaul paid the $25, brought it out to the east and had it tanned and dressed. He also made $125,000 in the mining market as a by-product of his visit to Yellowknife. So he had a sentimental affection for the great bear.

"See? Here's another," he exclaimed, as we knelt. "I have counted eleven of them."

"When did you first notice them?"

"Sometime after Christmas," said McCaul. "Then a couple at a time . . ."

"They look," I remarked, as we knelt on the rug, "as if they were snipped off by a knife. Or *scissors!*"

The word scissors had hardly left my mouth when I scrambled to my feet.

"Mac," I asked carefully, "who do you usually have in here visiting?"

"Oh, Bill Anderson, Harry Gatsby, Dr. Hall, Tom Jewell . . ."

"Tom Jewell!" I cried.

Tom Jewell is not only the greatest master of the fly rod of our time. He has not only taught scores of us how to cast. He is not only the author of the imperishable proposition that next to the violin, the split cane fly rod is the most perfect instrument conceived by man. He is *also* the greatest fly tier, salmon or trout, amongst the whole foregathering of us. He not only ties flies. He *invents* them.

"Call Tom," I said to McCaul. "Call him right now! Tell him I am here, and you're going to make a few Spanish onion and cheese sandwiches to go along with some Danish beer. Invite him over . . ."

"What the . . .?" asked McCaul.

"Quick," I pleaded. "See if he's in. See if he'll come. *Then* we'll go into action!"

"But I don't get it," said McCaul, getting up off the polar bear rug.

He called. Tom was in. Tom would be right over.

McCaul's house being old-fashioned, it has transoms over doors. There was a transom over the library door into the hall.

"Have you got a stepladder?" I begged.

"I've got a stepladder in the cellar, and an extension ladder in the garage."

"Good! I'll go down and get the stepladder," I said, "and you bring in the shortest section of the extension."

"What the . . .?" repeated McCaul.

"Does that transom open? Or has it been stuck with paint for 40 years?"

"It opens," said McCaul.

And he went and pulled the rod. It opened.

"All the way!" I commanded.

And he pulled it full down.

I dashed for the cellar. McCaul was coming in with the section of the extension ladder as I emerged from the stairs. We placed the two ladders on either side of the library door in the hall.

"If Tom happens to notice them," I instructed McCaul, "just say you are having some repairs done, or something . . ."

Hardly had we got back to our chairs when the bell rang, and there was good old Tom in his natty tweed jacket and his Tyrol hat.

He joined us. We chatted about the coming fishing season, a subject in which McCaul was not the least interested. Tom offered to walk the three blocks over to his house and bring over some colour slides of the steelhead trout he had caught last year in northern B.C. McCaul countered by threatening to get out his projector and show some slides he had taken last winter at some mines he is interested in up in the Chibougamau country of Quebec. But I skilfully shied them both off. And time passed. And I suggested I go to the kitchen and prepare some Spanish onion and cheese sandwiches.

"No, no," said McCaul, promptly catching on. "You cut them too thick! I'll get them."

He left. I followed.

"We'll only be five minutes, Tom," I apologized.

I closed the hall door.

The minute we walked into the kitchen, I slipped off my shoes, and signalled McCaul to do likewise.

In our stocking feet, we crept soundlessly back through the hall. With every sign and signal of warning to each other, we climbed our ladders by stealth, and peered over the transom.

There was dear old Tom Jewell on his knees, fondly stroking the polar bear's magnificent mantle. In one hand he had a few little glassine envelopes. In the other, a pair of small snub-nosed scissors. Expertly, he took a pinch of fur, about the size of a cigarette, and snipped it loose. He placed the loot in a glassine envelope.

He was just about to take the second snip when Mc-Caul let go.

"*Tommmmmmm!*" he bellowed from the transom.

Tom fell back into a sitting position, his face white with horror.

We scrambled down and came and stood over him.

Oh, yes. There was a little bad temper from McCaul as he declaimed on how valuable the great pelt was, how his heart was breaking over the mystery, how the bear rug was a lucky symbol to him . . .

And then as we stared down at Tom squatted on the rug, we all realized that we were old friends; and we started laughing, and hoisted Tom to his feet, all flushed and perspiring.

Now here is the deal we settled on, before all *three* of us went to the kitchen to make the Spanish onion and cheese sandwiches:

(A) Tom promises on his honour never to take another snip from the bear rug;

(B) Tom agrees to pay the $50 the fur dealer will charge for dressing up the snipped spots;

(C) As the mastermind who solved the mystery, I am to have the pick of six polar bear streamer trout flies from Tom's fly boxes. No cheating.

Finally, I have to confess that the reason I was able to solve the mystery of the snippets taken from the polar bear rug was that I had often thought of doing it myself.

Coward in the Corridor

The rumpus started at 10:30 P.M.

I looked at my watch. I was in bed in my hotel room, reading myself sweetly to sleep.

All of a sudden, somebody in an adjoining or nearby room turned on the TV at full BLAST.

It was shocking. The oompah-oompah of the music, the thump and boom of the unintelligible speaking voices made my bedroom quiver.

I sat up. I waited for them to turn the darn thing down. They didn't.

Now, there were two things I could do. I could reach for the house telephone on my bedside table and dial No. 1. This would give me the night manager, and I could utter my complaint in no uncertain terms.

Or, by golly, I could nip out of bed, take a quick peek out my door to discover which room was guilty of the uproar. Then I could nip back into bed, dial No. 7, and thereupon dial the room number of the disturber.

And could I give HIM a blast! Anonymously.

I think a man is more indignant at 10:30 P.M. than at the other hours of the day. Anyway, I chose the second course. I swung off the bed. I stepped softly to my door. The din was still booming. I opened my door.

There was nobody in sight in the corridor either way. I leaned out a little farther.

The racket was coming from room 680. My room is 683.

Hah!

Even in the uproar I heard a soft clunk and a snick behind me. I whirled.

It was too late. The breeze from my window had blown

the door shut. I was locked out of my room, in my bare feet and purple and white striped pyjamas. In the public corridor of this dear old hotel.

Now, what would you have done in a similar predicament?

I will tell you what I did. I panicked.

The corridor was loud with the TV program from 680. Should I slip quickly along to 680, demand that they turn down the TV and then ask permission to use their phone to call the bell captain to bring the pass key and let me back home?

No. Maybe the guy would slam the door in my face.

Should I risk tapping at the door next to me, explain in a gentlemanly fashion my situation and ask permission to use their phone?

No, maybe my next door neighbour was a lady, maybe a middle aged lady, maybe a spinster. Seeing a gentleman in purple and white striped pyjamas and his bare feet at her door, she would shriek, slam the door and telephone for the house-detective.

It is astonishing the paralysis that overtakes your wits in certain plights.

The elevators are in a little corridor about sixty paces from my room. I heard an elevator's doors above the TV racket.

Three ladies emerged from the elevator corridor and turned along the corridor towards me. I glued myself to my door. But I realized in a moment they would see me.

They passed me in silence.

"WOO-HOO," hooted one of the ladies, after they got by. "I wonder where HE's been!"

They vanished full of laughter and snorts up the corridor to the far turn.

Less than forty feet from me, a door opened, and a man stepped out.

"Thank heaven!" I exclaimed.

He halted and stared at me. Then he slowly approached.

He was one of those thick-set, ruddy-faced men with hard, humorous blue eyes. Dear friends, if you are ever in trouble and meet a thick-set, ruddy-faced man with humorous hard blue eyes, don't trust him!

When he stopped before me as I cringed at my door, I explained what had happened. The din was still booming from 680.

"Could you," I asked, "please nip back into your room and call the bell captain to come with the pass key?"

"Sorry old chap," he said, hilariously, "but I'm on my way down to meet some friends in the lobby. It will be just as quick for me to speak to the bell captain."

"Thank you, thank you!" I said fervently.

There I stood with my back flat against my door. Two minutes passed. Three. Then I heard the elevator, and around the corner came my thick-set, ruddy-faced, hard, humorous blue-eyed friend with three ladies and two men.

"There he is!" one of them cried.

And they advanced on me. They formed a delighted ring around me and asked me to repeat the circumstances in which I found myself.

"Did you," I begged of the thick-set fellow, "tell the bell captain?"

"By George, I forgot!" he exclaimed. "But I'll do it from my room right away."

"Would you," I asked, "rap on the door of 680 and tell them to turn down that damn TV?"

It was still throbbing the air.

"Oh, no," said he. "That is a matter for the hotel staff, don't you think?"

And he led his hearty and whooping friends along the corridor to his room.

I stood waiting.

No bell captain.

Every half minute either one of the ladies or one of the men from my thick-set, ruddy-faced, hard, humorous blue-eyed friend's room would peep out of the door.

"He's still THERE!" the ladies would squeak.

And gales of laughter would add to the rumpus of the TV.

Twice I heard the elevator doors, and twice parties came out of the elevator corridor but turned west, away from me.

But all things come to an end. I heard the elevator. A man appeared and turned my way. As he neared, I saw to my joy that he was a clergyman with his white collar.

Like the Prodigal Son, or the man who had fallen among thieves, I raised my hands to him.

"My poor chap!" he said.

"Swiftly, briefly, I explained my plight. I was by now getting pretty good at it.

"Come in!" said he.

He was my next door neighbour! I raced to the house phone. I dialled the bell captain. It was Mike, the night bell captain.

"I'm locked out!" I cried. "Bring your pass key! Quick!"

He was up in a minute.

From the clergyman's door, slightly ajar, I saw Mike approach, and I stepped forth.

"My gosh!" said Mike.

And let me in my room.

"Listen," I said, falling into a chair, "to that TV in 680 . . ."

"I'll fix it," said Mike, smiling out my door.

In a moment the blessed silence fell. The TV was stilled.

I waited five minutes and then phoned Mike again.

"Who the hell was it?" I asked.

"A dear old lady," said Mike, "from Edmonton. She's en route to Expo 67 by easy stages. She wears a hearing aid. But back home, she likes to turn her TV on full blast and leave her hearing aid off. She didn't realize it would disturb people here . . ."

"Dear old ladies!" I said bitterly. "Good-night, Mike!"

Mr. Penobscot

"Mr. Clark?" asked a crisp secretarial voice on the phone.
"Yes?"

"Mr. Penobscot on the line," said she.

"Mr. WHO?" I cried sharply.

But I was too late.

She had snicked over.

"Hello, Greg," came a warm, vaguely familiar voice. "How are you, old man?"

"Fine," I said, "fine."

Penobscot! PENOBSCOT? Who the dickens?

"I hear," said the voice, "you are looking for a nice young Golden Retriever puppy?"

"Yes," I said, "my daughter has asked me to find her a good Golden Retriever puppy to take home to New York."

Dogs? Penobscot? My mind was racing to put together the clues. Penobscot is the name of a big river down in the State of Maine. It is NOT a HUMAN name.

"Well, now, Greg, as you know," he said, "I've been raising Labradors and Goldens for years. I haven't any for sale; but I'd love to help you find a good one, and tell you some of the things to look out for if you're buying retrievers."

"Thanks very much," said I.

Penobscot? What the . . .

"What are you doing right now?" he asked.

"Well, nothing, actually," I said, very foolishly.

"Now look," said he. "I'm in the Trust Company building not a block from your hotel. I've got half an hour before I have to get off to a golf game. My office here is crowded with pictures of all the great Labradors and Goldens I have raised. Now look! You run over right away, like a good chap, and I'll take a load off your mind."

"Well, I . . . um," I flustered.

"Tenth floor," he said.

"What's your room number?"

"Oh, we have the whole floor," he said. "The receptionist right in front of the elevator will show you in."

He hung up, very executive.

Penobscot?

I put my hat on and took my stick. I went down the
elevator, walked the block, went up the Trust Company
elevator to the 10th floor.

And on the way up, I FORGOT THE NAME!

Now, I realize this will be difficult for you to believe.
But when you get up into the seventies, it is astonishing
how completely you will forget a name, forget a fact, forget
almost anything. Indeed, when you are seventy-five, you
will often hurry upstairs to your library on some sudden
and important mission, and on arriving, forget entirely
what the Sam Hill you had hurried up for.

So there I stepped out of the elevator into a beautiful,
posh, spacious executive floor of some big corporation, by
the look of it. My mind had that blank feeling you get
when you realize you have forgotten something. I glanced
around to see if there was some company name, some hint
of where I was. There was nothing. Just a lovely quiet
corridor, with pale green wall-to-wall broadloom and
handsome dark doors to many offices.

And there, all alone, facing me, sat a very pretty young
lady at a desk, smiling. The receptionist.

"May I help you?" she asked, as I came slowly forward.

"I have come to see a man," I said, "about a dog."

"What is the gentleman's name?"

"I'm sorry," I said. "It's on the tip of my tongue, but I
can't remember. It sounds like one of the rivers in
Maine?"

"Maine?" she said. "Well, I'm a Maritimer."

"Would it be something," I said, "like Kennybuck-tooth?"

"No, no," she smiled. "The Kennebec river is in Maine, all right; but Buctouche is a little town in New Brunswick."

"It doesn't suggest anybody around here?" I queried.

"This friend of mine phoned me not twenty minutes ago to run in and see him. He's got pictures of Labradors and Golden Retrievers all over his office wall. Does that help?"

"I'm sorry," she smiled, "but they are ALL dog men around here. From the president down to the juniors, they are all mad about dogs."

"Would it be Susquehanna?" I hazarded, thinking furiously.

"No, the Susquehanna is in Pennsylvania," she said. "My husband and I drove along it last summer on our holidays."

"You've got no Mr. Hannah?" I asked, hopefully.

"No Mr. Hannah," she said, her manner changing slightly.

I think she was beginning to think I was some old panhandler trying to cadge my way into any one of the executives she is employed to guard with her wits and her life.

I felt my tie. It was straight in my collar. I held my hat in front of me while I furtively swept a hand across my fly. It was zipped. We old fellows sometimes get a little frowsy-looking without realizing it.

"Well," I said, "I'm sorry. My friend's secretary, a young lady, gave me the name when she put in the call only a few minutes ago . . ."

Suddenly, like a light coming on in a dark cellar room, I had it!

"I've got it! I've GOT it!" I cried to the young lady. "Penobscot!"

"Penobscot?" she said. "Yes, there is a river in Maine of

that name. But it doesn't suggest anybody on THIS floor."

At which moment, a door at the far end of the beautiful corridor opened, and there was Harry McLaren.

"Greg!" he hailed. "I've been waiting for you. Come along, old boy."

I glanced gracefully at the pretty young lady and she looked shocked. I walked along and joined Harry and we went into his palatial office. There were fifty dog pictures on the walls. There were small retriever statues and large retriever statues on his desk, on side desks, on brackets up the walls.

I've known Harry for forty years, fishing, and at sports club meetings and around town. But I never knew what he did.

"What the heck," I enquired, gazing around the room, "do you do besides raise retrievers."

"Hell," he said, "I'm the president here."

And there for twenty minutes I sat and learned more about retrievers than either I or my daughter will ever need to know. And I got a list of all the leading kennels. And a list of all the points to watch for in picking a puppy. (You watch the kennel manager, not the puppies.)

And in came Harry's secretary with some last-minute letters to be signed.

"Young lady," I said, while Harry scrawled his signature, "when you called me a little while ago, you said to me that a Mr. Penobscot was coming on the line."

"Penobscot?" she protested. "Oh, yes, I remember. I have an allergy. And just as I said Mr. McLaren, I sneezed. I HOPE it didn't cause you any trouble."

"None whatever," I assured her gallantly, for she was blushing.

On the way out, I paused and explained the whole thing to the pretty young receptionist! And even if I DO look a little frowsy, we had a good laugh. And that's how you make friends.

Laugh.

My Youth As a Hippy

Sixty-five years ago, when all the world was young, we had hippies and beatniks. Only we didn't call them that. We called them daffy.

Some people appear to think that hippies and beatniks are new, a modern phenomenon. They have always been with us. You can see them on the ancient Greek friezes and on the wall paintings in the ruins of Pompeii. In the past as in the present, they were few in number. They got the publicity they did because they were good material for Grecian urns, or modern newspaper headings and bits on the TV and newsreel, when nothing better turns up.

Sixty-five years ago, when my friends and I smoked the whole wicker baby carriage, there would be one or two hippies in every village and town, and maybe a dozen or two in a city. But in those days there was no easy way for them to foregather, or coagulate, as you might say. That means to clot. If you were hippy or beatnik inclined, which means you were lazy and dreamy and rebellious, you couldn't simply go down to the town outskirts and thumb a ride to the nearest city. The only means of transportation was by railroad; and that cost money. None of the hippies I knew in my boyhood ever had any money. They were too poetical, too dreamy, to have a dollar; and too timid to ride the rods under a way-freight.

They were, as I realize now, simply delayed juveniles. Not retarded, mind you. Just delayed. It takes them until the age of twenty or more to reach the age at which my friends and I smoked that entire baby carriage, which was around twelve to fourteen.

Our group were Indians. We were the Iroquois Federation, the whole eleven of us. Personally, I was a Mohawk. I
was also the Medicine Man. But we had Iroquois, Seneca,
Onondaga and Cayuga, one or two of each. Our headquarters was a vacant lot on Brunswick avenue, where some
builder had excavated the cellar for a house, and then
abandoned it. The lot was beautifully forested with weeds,
mullein, burdock and white clover—perfect for a wilderness. In the wall of the excavation, we dug out a cave and
shored it up with bits of plank. As our tribe increased, we
erected a teepee in the best likeness of Ernest Thompson
Seton's *Two Little Savages*, made from sheets and other
cloth we were able to pinch from home or from neigh-
bouring clotheslines.

I don't know what the current hippies believe in. This
past summer, I managed to make the acquaintance of up
to a dozen of them. But in conversation, I came to the
conclusion that I was back in my boyhood, and that they
were Indians but didn't know it. From New York I got
friends to send me hippy literature; and from Berkeley in
California, several academics of my acquaintance sent me
odd looking little hippy newspapers and sheaves of hippy
poetry.

So I can assure you that no hippy, in his shabby clothes
and long flamboyantly dirty hair and skimpy beard, ever
strides in sandalled feet up the back streets filled with such
secret fervour as we Iroquois did long years ago in our
imaginary moccasins, late for supper. Like the hippies, we
tried to grow long hair, so that a feather would stick in it.
But in those days parents were more dominant than today.
We had to get it cut; and they gave us the ten cents for it,
too. In the second year of our Iroquois Federation, we got
hold of the works of Francis Parkman, illustrated. And
there we saw the true Iroquois coiffure—a stiff band of
upright hair in the middle of the scalp, the rest of the skull
clipped close. So we invented—or adopted—what was
known as the Brush Cut. And we got the barber to leave a

stiff brush up the middle, clipping the sides short. This lasted only overnight. For even I, the Medicine Man, was sent back to the barber, to have the whole skull evenly trimmed.

Like the hippies, we tried to be smoky, if not dirty. We had, of course, our council fire, which we lit in the cave. Not too large, for fear of attracting the attention of the neighbours or the passing cop on his bicycle. For smoking, we tried everything. Cedar bark, stripped off the fence posts of various back yards, was the principle material consumed, though we tried bracken leaves in season, oak leaves, and sundry others. We never came on pot.

But the effect was no doubt the same. We saw visions and dreamed dreams, as do all hippies and small boys. We used toilet paper to make our cigarettes of cedar bark or fern. I do not know what the hippies use, though they tell me they use sugar cubes to put LSD on, in order to go on "trips." We often saw gentlemen of the neighbourhood going home in the evening on "trips," full of beer or whisky. But of that we knew nothing. We could only surmise.

It was on one of our forays—and if you saw our Federation on a foray, you would imagine it was nothing but a bunch of boys passing up the street—you would never be more wrong—on one of our forays up past St. Alban's Cathedral, we found a beautiful vacant lot, even fuller of burdocks, mulleins and white clover than our home forest. Into this, the neighbours had the habit of chucking anything that wouldn't go easily into the garbage can: worn out wash boilers, old pots and pans, laundry wringers that had lost their grip. It was an interesting place for a foray.

And there we found the wicker baby carriage. In the Victorian era of which I speak, the wicker baby carriage was THE fashion. It was constructed of some kind of cane, beautifully woven and braided and rolling in scrolls of wicker. It had high wheels and a silk parasol dangled over it. Most of our Federation had spent our infancy in such carriages, before the modern metallic age.

And here, in the dump, was this wicker treasure, damaged, I must confess, faded and worn from the rains and the winters that had passed over it all the years it may have lain amid the weeds. Rejected.

I think it was Cecil Perry, who was the Seneca and Sachem of the Federation, who hit upon a fantastic idea. He broke off a cigarette length piece of the tattered wicker work. He studied it. It was porous. It was cane, about pencil-thickness.

"How!" he commanded; and we gathered around him.

As Medicine Man, I had the match. Cecil lit the end of the cane. The smoke billowed out!

It was magnificent. We all hastily broke off fragments of the wicker, and soon we were all alight, seated in council amid the tall white clover and the mullein, around the baby carriage.

In the autumn dusk, we transported that baby carriage all the way back to our cave and teepee. It squeaked, and only one wheel really worked. But we were unmolested by our elders. That is the great thing: to be unmolested by elders.

And before Christmas, we had smoked that whole baby carriage. Nothing remained but the bent and rusted wheels and the twisted frame. Even the thin boards that had been the cushion base, we used for our council fires. We sold the metal remains to a passing rags, bones and bottles man for four cents.

But all things came to an end, as the hippies will find out. People grow up. Visions fade. Dreams vanish. When the Iroquois Federation got into high school, we had to graduate into long pants. Within a year, none of the eleven of us would even mention the old cave or the teepee. Or the baby carriage. It was as if we were ashamed of them. Within six years, five of the eleven were dead, killed in action in World War I.

And some of us became prosperous merchants, and one a lawyer, and one a newspaperman.

What Is It With You?

With me, it is parsnips.

What is it with you?

I HATE parsnips. I have hated them for sixty-five years.

I hate the taste of them. I hate the smell of them. I hate the sight of them naked on the counter in the grocery store, pallid great obscene carrots, with dirt in all the wrinkles of their skins.

When I was a child, we had few green vegetables. As autumn came, we had to depend on potatoes, turnips, carrots, parsnips and things that could be kept in root cellars.

And, being the eldest child in the family, I had to set an example of behaviour and acceptance for my younger brother and sister. I had to eat parsnips. It must have been very early in my life that I took this scunner to them. How I gagged them down, creamed, roasted, glazed, I can only imagine.

I was ten years old when I rebelled. In glorious technicolour, I can recall in lovely memory the hour that I became a man.

My father sat at the head of the dining room table, serving the meat. My mother sat at the opposite end, serving the vegetables. Across the white-clothed table sat my Grandma and my three-year-old sister. Beside me sat my younger brother, Little Joe. Behind my mother stood Bella Duggan, the cook-maid, in her little white cap and small white apron, to hand the plates around.

Grandma was served first, then my little sister. I came third.

When Bella Duggan handed my mother my plate. I said:

"No parsnips, please."

"No WHAT!" exclaimed my mother, staring at me.

"No," I said in a small clear voice that I can still hear in memory across the many, many years, "parsnips."

There was a shocked silence. Bella Duggan, my old friend and counsellor, stared at me over my mother's shoulder.

"OF COURSE you will have parsnips," said my mother, and spooned a couple of dollops of creamed parsnips onto my plate.

Bella Duggan brought it around and set it before me.

It was the moment of truth for a child.

The children chattered; my father and mother and Grandma chatted across the table, and I pushed the parsnips over to the edge of my plate. In memory, I think I did not lower my eyes. I like to remember that I ate my dinner and tried to catch my mother's bright blue eyes, or the golden amber eyes of my father. But our eyes did not meet. My dinner finished, there sat the parsnips on the side of my plate; and when I caught my father's eyes, he gave me a wry, shy smile.

From that night on, whenever we had parsnips, my mother would explain to Bella Duggan, as she served me the other vegetables, as a sort of society news:

"Gregory does not take parsnips."

This recollection came back to me yesterday morning when I was having breakfast in the cafeteria of the lovely old hotel where I now live. I. E. Ted Jones, an investment dealer who often has breakfast with me, came and joined me at the table. He had, as usual, his glass of orange juice, the toasted bacon sandwich, the marmalade and the pot of coffee.

A waitress came with a tray and set it down for another man at the adjoining table.

I was surprised to see Jones suddenly shift his position and sit with his back to the newcomer. In his eyes was an expression I had never noticed before.

"Anything wrong?" I enquired discreetly, in a quiet voice.

Ted Jones is a most courteous and kindly man. He leaned towards me.

"He is having PORRIDGE!" he said, equally quiet.

So I waited until the stranger, a quick man, had engulfed his porridge, munched his toast, quaffed his coffee, and in the fashion of our time, hustled off on his way.

"Porridge," I said to Ted Jones.

"I hate it!" said Ted, his eyes flashing. "I hate the SIGHT of it!"

"Hmmmm," I invited.

"When I was ten," said Ted, "my mother set the usual bowl of rolled oats porridge before me. My mother was a tall, fair haired woman of great force of character. I looked up at her and simply said, 'I won't eat it!' "

"Ten?" I asked.

"Yes," said Jones. "I was ten. If I recall, I had fought for eighteen months or more to get up the courage to tell my mother I would not eat the stuff any more. Then I did it."

"What happened?"

"I took a terrible and unforgettable scolding. The other children watched me. But I stood fast. And I never ate porridge again. And never will!"

And somehow, Ted Jones appeared before me as a little boy, not a man in his fifties. There was the fey look of remembrance about him.

So I then told him the story I have told you about parsnips.

And then I told him the REST of the story about parsnips!

When I grew up and left home and started travelling the world as a reporter and eating my meals even in my home city in various restaurants, whenever I saw parsnips on the menu, I ORDERED them.

"Ah," I would say to the waiter, giving my order, "and bring me a side dish of parsnips! Not on my plate, you understand, but a SIDE dish, a good big side dish of parsnips!"

"Yessir," the waiter would say, recognizing that he had a parsnip lover on his hands.

When my meal is served, I quickly take the side dish of parsnips and put them as far away from me on the table as I can reach.

And there I let the darn things sit while I smile through my dinner.

They sit there and grow cold; and when I have gone, they are thrown out.

Ted Jones was watching me with an amused expression.

"Not really," he said. "You don't STILL do that!"

"Yes, I do," I said. "I like to be ten again. I like to recapture in this childish act the feeling of authority, of the sudden move from childhood to manhood that I experienced at the moment so many years ago."

Jones looked off into space.

"I would hate to try it with porridge," he said.

"Try it," I urged. "It is the way you exorcise ghosts. It is the way you obliterate unhappy memories. Take out and put before you the thing you detest, the thing you hate, even, and smile at it."

"Eeech!" shivered Jones.

"A smile," I quoted somebody from the past, "is the deadliest dagger in the armament of man."

"Who said that?" asked Ted Jones.

"I don't remember," I replied.

THIS morning, when I went for breakfast in the cafeteria, there sat my friend at the accustomed table.

He had his usual toasted bacon sandwich.

On the far edge of the table, largely hidden from him by the sugar caster and other implements that Maria, our witty Austrian waitress, had arranged around it, sat a bowl of oatmeal porridge.

It was, I could see, already cold. The silver brown-sugar bowl, the cream jug leaned against it. It was rejected.

"I may get used to it," said Jones. "But do you know something? I believe it works. I am smiling now at something I have not smiled at in forty years. A memory!"

Big Blondes

Gentlemen prefer blondes, so they say.

If that is true, I am no gentleman.

I have been terrorized by blondes ever since September 25, 1898.

It is all due to a trauma, which I will explain in a minute.

By blondes, I don't mean those small slim ones. I mean the big bulgey ones. For ten years, during the reign of the late Marilyn Monroe, the late Jayne Mansfield and the still current Anita Ekberg, I had been unable to go to the movies. I would have had to be led smothering from the theatre, had one of them appeared on the screen. All on account of my trauma.

September 25, 1898, was my sixth birthday. My parents' house was filled with aunties that day. And a couple of next door neighbours who had dropped in on the girls.

One of those neighbours was my Nemesis, fair, fat and thirty.

In 1898, there were no motor cars, no highways. My aunties from various country towns round-about arrived by train at this season. It was pickling time. And they came and visited, to help my mother with the pickling and at the same time to do their shopping for their winter wardrobes, their husbands' long-handled underwear, and the children's.

In this kitchen that fateful morning were my mother Sarah, my Grandma Louisa, my Aunt Lib, Aunt Nan,

Aunt Mart, and Mrs. Taylor from next door, and Mrs. Cassidy from across the street.

I request you to keep a sharp eye on this Mrs. Cassidy during what follows.

My father had come upstairs to the attic room where my three-year-old brother Little Joe and I slept, to keep us there until we were called to the birthday breakfast. I knew, of course, it was my birthday, and we could hear the sounds of all my aunties below as they dressed and prepared. At 8 A.M. we were called. The dining room table was bright with a birthday cake and six candles, flowers and my gifts – three black iron horses drawing a nickel-plated fire engine as big as a coffee mug; an Indian head-dress made of turkey feathers; new slippers, a new sweater, a box of chocolates with shiny red roses on the lid.

My mother, my Grandma and all my aunties gathered round, and there was great excitement, as Little Joe, who did not understand about birthdays at age three, was furious at having nothing while I had so much; and he howled and yelled. Though this was seventy years ago, I remember it all as though it were last week. My father was happy to gobble his breakfast and leave for the office to get out of the tumult.

An important factor in the disaster that followed is that my mother had to take Little Joe upstairs to change him, as in his fury he had so far forgotten himself as to wet his pants. It was there that I decided to carry my birthday presents out to the back yard and put them up on the fence scantling, out of range of Little Joe when he came downstairs. My arms loaded with my gifts, I worked my way through the crowd of all my aunties in the kitchen. And with my elbow, I pushed open the screen door.

There was a small back stoop, with three steps down to the ground level. On the side to which I had my back, as I pushed the screen door, was a cellar window. It was let down into the foundations in a wooden chute.

The window had four panes of glass.

I stepped back to clear my laden arms of the screen door.

I stepped into space.

Down I went into the cellar window-way. All in a ball, I hit the cellar window and burst it from its nails.

Down we went, the window, frame, glass and all, on top of a six-gallon crock of pickles in brine that my Grandma was maturing. It sat on the plank cellar floor.

We smashed it to smithereens. There was glass, frame, pickles, fractured crock, brine, a tremendous crash, and me, unharmed amid all the riot.

At age six, you are allowed to yell. And as I yelled, I could hear the great thunder of feet on the kitchen floor above.

The first to arrive was Mrs. Cassidy from across the road. She had only come in and had not yet been served her first cup of tea.

Down the stairs she bounced, a great, blonde young woman (as I now know she must have been) generously endowed, as the movie critics used to say of Jayne Mansfield. My aunties came tumbling behind her. She was the first.

She snatched me screaming up out of the wreckage and hugged me to her bosom. I had lost my birthday presents in the crash. It has often occurred to me, long since, that if I had had my iron horse fire engine in my arms, I would have been spared what happened to me. I would have no trauma to this day.

A trauma, says the dictionary, is a startling experience which has a lasting effect on the mind.

Mrs. Cassidy hugged me to her ample breast. My aunties were screaming and exclaiming around us, sure that I had been injured. The more I screamed, the more Mrs. Cassidy hugged. She cut off my wind. I will remember this to my dying day. The more I fought, the tighter she clutched. I was smothering. My head felt as if it was about to burst. I must very nearly have lost consciousness in that awful embrace. Then my mother dashed down the stairs.

She snatched me from Mrs. Cassidy's arms just in the nick of time. According to my Grandma Louisa and various aunties who often told me a replay of the incident, I gave four or five enormous hoarse gasps and then burst into screams again.

"I couldn't breathe!" I yelled. "She squashed me! She squashed me!"

And when poor Mrs. Cassidy drew near, I stared in terror and then turned away and clung to my mother.

"I couldn't breathe!" I wailed, as she carried me all wet with pickle brine, up the cellar stairs, to undress me and see if I had suffered any cuts, bruises or wrenches as the result of my magnificent fall. Miraculously, I had none.

My aunties and grandma stayed down to clean up the wreckage and all those pickle scattered all over the place. Auntie Mart stepped on a gherkin, skidded, and sat down with a thump, spraining her ankle. The only casualty of the whole episode.

Except my trauma.

Mrs. Cassidy, who was childless, used to pick up Little Joe and me two or three times a week and take us for a walk to the shopping corner two blocks away.

She never picked me up again. At the very sight of her, I would run and hide in the furnace cellar, or rush to the foot of the yard, climb up and over the back fence and peep through a crack in the planks until I saw her depart with Little Joe.

There was no trauma about the fall through the window, or all those pickles. In the two wars, I have been blown up, buried, crashed, torpedoed, and flung all over, without the slightest concern. And I love pickles.

But, oh, that other trauma! We moved away before my eighth birthday to a new district, and I lost Mrs. Cassidy. On the new street were two very bulgey blonde ladies whom I was able to evade by skilful footwork. At my new

school, I was put into the class of Miss Fell, who was ter-
rific. I was so inattentive in class, spending all my time
staring out the window and quietly smothering to death
that, at the end of the first week, I was sent home at noon
with a note to my parents suggesting that I was in need of
medical attention. Of course, by this time, my prejudices
were a laughing matter to my parents, aunties and their
friends. My mother telephoned my father to come home
for lunch. He read the note.

We went down to the end of the garden for a man to
man talk.

"What seems to be the matter, son?" my father, a laughing man, asked.

"Miss Fell has a big boom," I said, brokenly.

"Not boom, son," corrected Old Joe, my dad. "It is BOO-
zum! You pronounce it BOO-zum."

"Yes, sir," said I penitently.

But boom it will be. Boom it has been for seventy
years. And boom it will remain to the day I die.

My father accompanied me back to school after lunch,
and while I stood out in the corridor, my father held a
private conversation with the principal, a most understanding little man. I was transferred from Miss Fell's class
to that of a tall, slim teacher, flat as an ironing board. My
scholarship improved fantastically and within a month, I
was teacher's pet. (I have the curious impression that I
have been teacher's pet ever since.)

I am ashamed to confess how many times in my youth
and manhood I have shifted my seat in buses, street cars
trains, aircraft, restaurants. I confess I have, in my time,
even got off a bus, if there were two or three of them on
it.

Boom it was, boom it will always be. I was forty years
old before I encountered a book on psychiatry and trauma.
I read it with the greatest delight. My mind rationalized
my condition. But there is something deeper than the
mind in us. There is something ancient in the spirit of

man. My mind laughed. But still I smothered.

So, dear ladies who are generously endowed, if whenever we meet and I appear rude, and rear back and seem to be smothering, please forgive me. It is not a man who is frightened of you.

It is only a little child.

"They Might Be Looking out Their Windows"

Tomorrow and Monday, we shall be observing the fiftieth anniversary of Armistice Day, each in our accustomed fashion.

Before I tell the parable of the One Block Of Howland Avenue, may I remind you that the first Armistice Day, half a century ago, was one of wild jubilation on the one hand and, in 60,000 Canadian homes, one of blinds-drawn, door-locked intense sorrow and mourning.

That first Armistice Day, while those of us surviving the four years' war of filth and futility laid down our weapons in a kind of stupor of disbelief and walked on top of ground to stare at a stilled world, the rest of the world went almost mad with jubilation. In London, Paris, New York and in all lesser cities, it was pandemonium. The War To End War had ended!

Now, we know it didn't.

So tomorrow and Monday, fifty broken years later, we will carry on as usual. Instead of the jubilation of the vast majority of that former time, the majority of us now will count Armistice Day just another holiday. We will take a last autumn weekend at the cottage. We will go on hunting parties. We'll relax, not jubilate. The merchants will keep their stores busier than ever on this strategically-spaced mercantile solstice marking the end of autumn and the start of winter shopping.

Wherever there are cenotaphs or other war memorials in city and town, small groups of a few hundred will gather briefly for ceremonies.

And that one minute of silence!

No, I am not bitter.

Howland Avenue is a short street in Toronto, four blocks in length, running north from Bloor Street, which is a main cross-town artery to Davenport Road, another cross-town.

It is the first block, from Bloor to Barton Avenue, to which I refer. There are about 35 houses on either side. It is a tree-bowered, quiet street. Businessmen, professors of the university, editors, a doctor or two lived on it in my time. A rather comfortable street.

I do not know how it celebrated that first Armistice Day. I wasn't there. In the previous years, the young men one by one had quietly slipped away to war.

My younger brother, Joe Junior, beat me to it. Then I followed. We were young civilians. When the war ended, we returned. Joe Junior was a Flight Commander in the RAF, wearing the Distinguished Flying Cross. I was an infantry officer, wearing the Military Cross. Number 66 Howland Avenue was a proud house that spring day when a party was held for all our relatives and friends to come and welcome us home.

We were in uniform still, of course.

We were hugged, kissed, slapped on the back. The house became crowded. Refreshments filled the dining room.

My father, Joseph T. Clark, editor, quietly signalled Joe Junior and me, amid the gaiety and chatter. We followed him upstairs to the front room, his library and den. He closed the door.

"Boys," he said, "I have a favour to ask you."

"Yes, sir!"

"I ask you," he said, his face tense, "not to walk up or down Howland Avenue. I want you to come to the house, from now on, by coming up either Albany or Brunswick" (the two adjoining avenues) "to Barton. Then along Barton here, and down to the house."

Our house was seven doors below Barton.

We stared at our Dad. He went over and kicked the cannel coal flickering in the fireplace, and pulled himself together.

"Starting at the bottom, at Bloor," he said, "Billy Hall, air force, killed in action."

We didn't know.

"Then," said our Dad, "up the street a few doors, this side, Captain Cecil Perry, artillery, killed in action."

"Oh, no!" I muttered.

"Across the street, up from the Perry's," continued our father. "Captain Bill and Lieutenant Jack McLaren, infantry, both killed in action."

He was naming all our boyhood playmates, our high school chums, the comrades of our young manhood.

Joe, my brother, sat down in the Morris chair and covered his eyes.

"Up the street, here, across the road," went on Dad, "the young fellow whose name I don't know, who boarded at 79, a student of engineering at the School Of Science, engineers, killed in action."

My father went over to the window and without parting the curtains, stared out at Howland Avenue.

From downstairs came the tumult of our party of welcome home.

All the young men of the one block of Howland Avenue were gone, except us.

How does an aging man, staring out a window, equate his pride at having his sons home and his grief for his long-time neighbours and friends?

"Sir," I said, when I could get my voice, "that is an order! And we will obey it."

"They might be looking out their windows," said Dad.

Joe Junior got up and went and put his arm around him.

Thus it was that we never walked up or down the first block of Howland Avenue.

We always marched swiftly up the seven doors to Barton.